Illustrative Mathematics

ALGEBRA 1

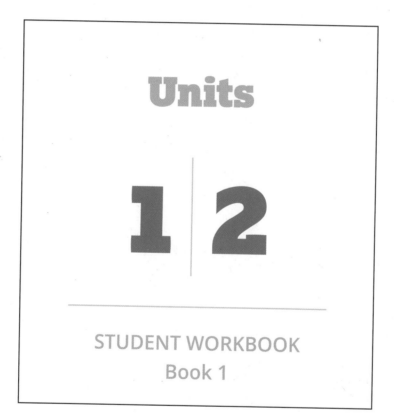

Units

1 | 2

STUDENT WORKBOOK
Book 1

ISBN 978-1-5249-9104-3

AGA1.0

Illustrative Mathematics

ALGEBRA 1

Unit

1

STUDENT WORKBOOK

Book 1

Lesson 1: Getting to Know You

- Let's work together to collect data and explore statistical questions.

1.1: Which One Doesn't Belong?: Types of Data

Which one doesn't belong?

Question A: How many potato chips are in this bag of chips?

Question B: What is the typical number of chips in a bag of chips?

Question C: What type of chips are these?

Question D: What type of chips do students in this class prefer?

1.2: Representing Data About You and Your Classmates

Your teacher will assign you a set of 3 questions.

- Write another question of your own that will require data collected from the class to answer.

- For each of the 4 questions, write a survey question that will help you collect data from the class that can be analyzed to answer the questions.

- Ask the 4 survey questions to 15 classmates and record their responses to collect data.

- After collecting the data return to your group.

1. What is the question of your own that will require data collected from the class to answer?

2. What are the 4 survey questions you will ask your classmates?

3. Summarize the data for each question in a sentence or two and share the results with your group.

4. With your group, decide what the responses for question number 1 have in common. Then do the same for questions numbered 2 and 3.

5. Does the question you wrote fit best with the questions from number 1, 2, or 3? Explain your reasoning.

responder's name	question 1 response	question 2 response	question 3 response	my question response

Are you ready for more?

1. Find a news article that uses numerical data to discuss a statistical question.

2. Find a news article that uses categorical data to discuss a statistical question.

Lesson 1 Summary

Statistics is about using data to solve problems or make decisions. There are two types of data:

- **Numerical data** are expressed using a number. For example, to answer the question "How tall are the students in this class?" you would measure the height of each student which would result in numerical data.

- **Categorical data** are expressed using characteristics. For example, to answer the question "What brand of phones do people use?" you would survey several people and their answers result in categorical data.

The question that you ask determines the type of data that you collect and whether or not there is *variability* in the data collected. In earlier grades, you learned that there is variability in a data set if all of the values in the data set are not the same. These are examples of **statistical questions** because they are answered by collecting data that has variability:

- "What is the average class size at this school?" would produce numerical data with some variability.

- "What are the favorite colors of students in this class?" would produce categorical data with some variability.

These are examples **non-statistical questions** because they are answered by collecting data that does not vary:

- "How many students are on the roster for this class?" would produce numerical data that does not vary. There is only one value in the data set, so there is no variability.

- "What color is this marker?" would produce categorical data that does not vary. There is only one value in the data set, so there is no variability.

Glossary

- categorical data
- non-statistical question
- numerical data
- statistical question

Lesson 1 Practice Problems

1. Write a survey question for which you would expect to collect numerical data.

2. Write a survey question for which you would expect to collect categorical data.

3. Select **all** the statistical questions.

   A. What is the typical amount of rainfall for the month of June in the Galapagos Islands?

   B. How much did it rain yesterday at the Mexico City International Airport?

   C. Why do you like to listen to music?

   D. How many songs does the class usually listen to each day?

   E. How many songs did you listen to today?

   F. What is the capital of Canada?

   G. How long does it typically take for 2nd graders to walk a lap around the track?

Lesson 2: Data Representations

- Let's represent and analyze data using dot plots, histograms, and box plots.

2.1: Notice and Wonder: Battery Life

The dot plot, histogram, and box plot summarize the hours of battery life for 26 cell phones constantly streaming video. What do you notice? What do you wonder?

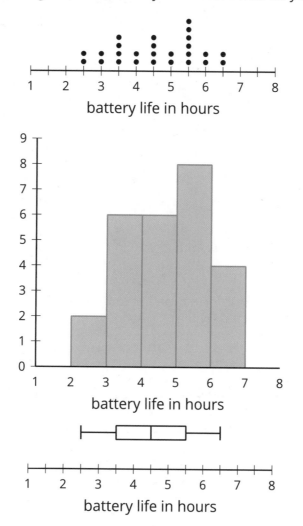

2.2: Tomato Plants: Histogram

A histogram can be used to represent the distribution of numerical data.

1. The data represent the number of days it takes for different tomato plants to produce tomatoes. Use the information to complete the frequency table.

47	52	53	55	57
60	61	62	63	65
65	65	65	68	70
72	72	75	75	75
76	77	78	80	81
82	85	88	89	90

days to produce fruit	frequency
40–50	
50–60	
60–70	
70–80	
80–90	
90–100	

2. Use the set of axes and the information in your table to create a histogram.

Algebra 1 iM KH

3. The histogram you created has intervals of width 10 (like 40–50 and 50–60). Use the set of axes and data to create another histogram with an interval of width 5. How does this histogram differ from the other one?

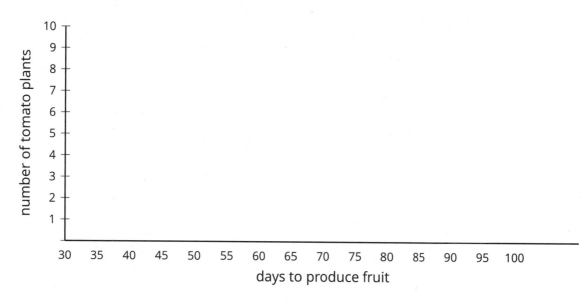

Are you ready for more?

It often takes some playing around with the interval lengths to figure out which gives the best sense of the shape of the distribution.

1. What might be a problem with using interval lengths that are too large?

2. What might be a problem with using interval lengths that are too small?

3. What other considerations might go into choosing the length of an interval?

2.3: Tomato Plants: Box Plot

A box plot can also be used to represent the distribution of numerical data.

minimum	Q1	median	Q3	maximum

1. Using the same data as the previous activity for tomato plants, find the median and add it to the table. What does the median represent for these data?

2. Find the median of the least 15 values to split the data into the first and second quarters. This value is called the first quartile. Add this value to the table under Q1. What does this value mean in this situation?

3. Find the value (the third quartile) that splits the data into the third and fourth quarters and add it to the table under Q3. Add the minimum and maximum values to the table.

4. Use the **five-number summary** to create a box plot that represents the number of days it takes for these tomato plants to produce tomatoes.

```
  +---+---+---+---+---+---+---+---+---+---+
  40  45  50  55  60  65  70  75  80  85  90
                time in days
```

Lesson 2 Summary

The table shows a list of the number of minutes people could intensely focus on a task before needing a break. 50 people of different ages are represented.

19	7	1	16	20	2	7	19
9	13	3	9	18	13	20	8
3	14	13	2	8	5	17	7
18	17	8	8	7	6	2	20
7	7	10	7	6	19	3	18
8	19	7	13	20	14	6	3
19	4						

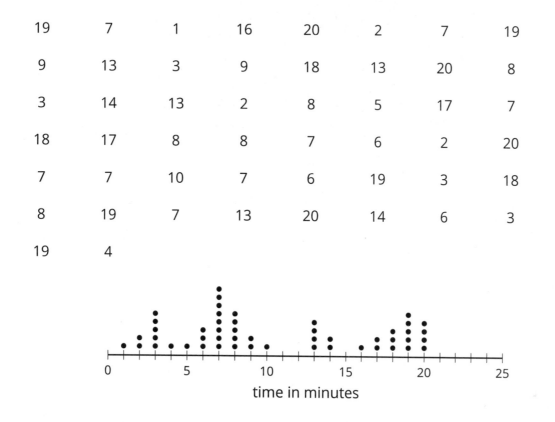

In a situation like this, it is helpful to represent the data graphically to better notice any patterns or other interesting features in the data. A dot plot can be used to see the shape and **distribution** of the data.

There were quite a few people that lost focus at around 3, 7, 13, and 19 minutes and nobody lost focus at 11, 12, or 15 minutes. Dot plots are useful when the data set is not too large and shows all of the individual values in the data set. In this example, a dot plot can easily show all the data. If the data set is very large (more than 100 values, for example) or if there are many different values that are not exactly the same, it may be hard to see all of the dots on a dot plot.

A histogram is another representation that shows the shape and distribution of the same data.

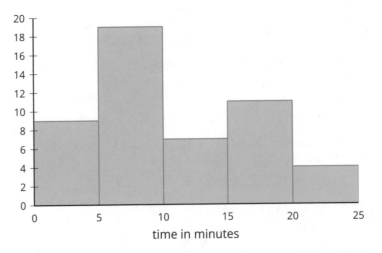

Most people lost focus between 5 and 10 minutes or between 15 and 20 minutes, while only 4 of the 50 people got distracted between 20 and 25 minutes. When creating histograms, each interval includes the number at the lower end of the interval but not the upper end. For example, the tallest bar displays values that are greater than or equal to 5 minutes but less than 10 minutes. In a histogram, values that are in an interval are grouped together. Although the individual values get lost with the grouping, a histogram can still show the shape of the distribution.

Here is a box plot that represents the same data.

Box plots are created using the **five-number summary**. For a set of data, the five-number summary consists of these five statistics: the minimum value, the first quartile, the median, the third quartile, and the maximum value. These values split the data into four sections each representing approximately one-fourth of the data. The median of this data is indicated at 8 minutes and about 25% of the data falls in the short second quarter of the data between 6 and 8 minutes. Similarly, approximately one-fourth of the data is between 8 and 17 minutes. Like the histogram, the box plot does not show individual data values, but other features such as quartiles, range, and median are seen more easily. Dot plots, histograms, and box plots provide 3 different ways to look at the shape and distribution while highlighting different aspects of the data.

Glossary

- distribution
- five-number summary

Lesson 2 Practice Problems

1. The dot plot displays the number of bushes in the yards for houses in a neighborhood. What is the median?

number of bushes

2. The data set represents the shoe sizes of 19 students in a fifth grade physical education class.

   4, 5, 5, 5, 6, 6, 6, 6, 7, 7, 7, 7, 7.5, 7.5, 8, 8, 8.5, 8.5, 9

   Create a box plot to represent the distribution of the data.

3. The data set represents the number of pages in the last book read by each of 20 students over the summer.

   163, 170, 171, 173, 175, 205, 220, 220, 220, 253, 267, 281, 305, 305, 305, 355, 371, 388, 402, 431

   Create a histogram to represent the distribution of the data.

4. Each set of data was collected from surveys to answer statistical questions. Select **all** of the data sets that represent numerical data.

    A. {1, 1.2, 1.4, 1.4, 1.5, 1.6, 1.8, 1.9, 2, 2, 2.1, 2.5}

    B. {Red, Red, Yellow, Yellow, Blue, Blue, Blue}

    C. {45, 60, 60, 70, 75, 80, 85, 90, 90, 100, 100, 100}

    D. {-7, -5, -3, -1, -1, -1, 0}

    E. {98.2, 98.4, 98.4, 98.6, 98.6, 98.6, 98.6, 98.7, 98.8, 98.8}

    F. {Yes, Yes, Yes, Yes, Maybe, Maybe, No, No, No}

    G. {A, A, A, B, B, B, C, C, C}

(From Unit 1, Lesson 1.)

5. Is "What is the typical distance a moped can be driven on a single tank of gas?" a statistical question? Explain your reasoning.

(From Unit 1, Lesson 1.)

Lesson 3: A Gallery of Data

- Let's make, compare, and interpret data displays.

3.1: Notice and Wonder: Dot Plots

The dot plots represent the distribution of the amount of tips, in dollars, left at 2 different restaurants on the same night.

What do you notice? What do you wonder?

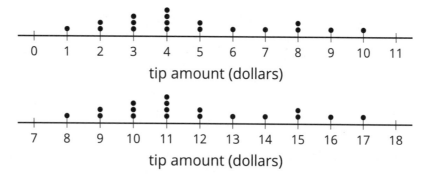

3.2: Data Displays

Your teacher will assign your group a statistical question. As a group:

1. Create a dot plot, histogram, and box plot to display the distribution of the data.

2. Write 3 comments that interpret the data.

As you visit each display, write a sentence or two summarizing the information in the display.

Are you ready for more?

Choose one of the more interesting questions you or a classmate asked and collect data from a larger group, such as more students from the school. Create a data display and compare results from the data collected in class.

Lesson 3 Summary

We can represent a distribution of data in several different forms, including lists, dot plots, histograms, and box plots. A list displays all of the values in a data set and can be organized in different ways. This list shows the pH for 30 different water samples.

5.9	7.6	7.5	8.2	7.6	8.6	8.1	7.9
6.1	6.3	6.9	7.1	8.4	6.5	7.2	6.8
7.3	8.1	5.8	7.5	7.1	8.4	8.0	7.2
7.4	6.5	6.8	7.0	7.4	7.6		

Here is the same list organized in order from least to greatest.

5.8	5.9	6.1	6.3	6.5	6.5	6.8	6.8
6.9	7.0	7.1	7.1	7.2	7.2	7.3	7.4
7.4	7.5	7.5	7.6	7.6	7.6	7.9	8.0
8.1	8.1	8.2	8.4	8.4	8.6		

With the list organized, you can more easily:

- interpret the data

- calculate the values of the five-number summary

- estimate or calculate the mean

- create a dot plot, box plot, or histogram

Here is a dot plot and histogram representing the distribution of the data in the list.

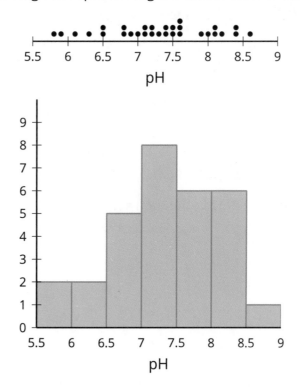

A dot plot is created by putting a dot for each value above the position on a number line. For the pH dot plot, there are 2 water samples with a pH of 6.5 and 1 water sample with a pH of 7. A histogram is made by counting the number of values from the data set in a certain interval and drawing a bar over that interval at a height that matches the count. In the pH histogram, there are 5 water samples that have a pH between 6.5 and 7 (including 6.5, but not 7). Here is a box plot representing the distribution of the same data as the dot plot and histogram.

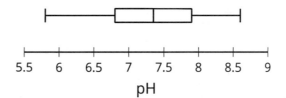

To create a box plot, you need to find the minimum, first quartile, median, third quartile, and maximum values for the data set. These 5 values are sometimes called the *five-number summary*. Drawing a vertical mark and then connecting the pieces as in the example creates the box plot. For the pH box plot, we can see that the minimum is about 5.8, the median is about 7.4, and the third quartile is around 7.9.

Lesson 3 Practice Problems

1. The box plot represents the distribution of speeds, in miles per hour, of 100 cars as they passed through a busy intersection.

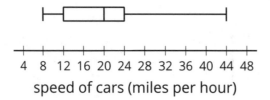

speed of cars (miles per hour)

a. What is the smallest value in the data set? Interpret this value in the situation.

b. What is the largest value in the data set? Interpret this value in the situation.

c. What is the median? Interpret this value in the situation.

d. What is the first quartile (Q1)? Interpret this value in the situation.

e. What is the third quartile (Q3)? Interpret this value in the situation.

2. The data set represents the number of eggs produced by a small group of chickens each day for ten days: 7, 7, 7, 7, 7, 8, 8, 8, 8, 9. Select **all** the values that could represent the typical number of eggs produced in a day.

   A. 7.5 eggs

   B. 7.6 eggs

   C. 7.7 eggs

   D. 8 eggs

   E. 9 eggs

3. The dot plot displays the lengths of pencils (in inches) used by students in a class. What is the mean?

length (inches)

(From Unit 1, Lesson 2.)

4. The histogram represents ages of 40 people at a store that sells children's clothes. Which interval contains the median?

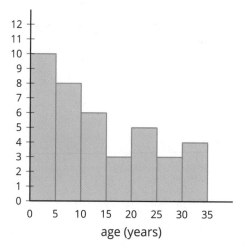

age (years)

   A. The interval from 0 to 5 years.

   B. The interval from 5 to 10 years.

   C. The interval from 10 to 15 years.

   D. The interval from 15 to 20 years.

(From Unit 1, Lesson 2.)

5. The data set represents the responses, in degrees Fahrenheit, collected to answer the question "How hot is the sidewalk during the school day?".

   92, 95, 95, 95, 98, 100, 100, 100, 103, 105, 105, 111, 112, 115, 115, 116, 117, 117, 118, 119, 119, 119, 119, 119, 119

   a. Create a dot plot to represent the distribution of the data.

   b. Create a histogram to represent the distribution of the data.

   c. Which display gives you a better overall understanding of the data? Explain your reasoning.

   (From Unit 1, Lesson 2.)

6. Is "What is the area of the floor in this classroom?" a statistical question? Explain your reasoning.

   (From Unit 1, Lesson 1.)

Lesson 4: The Shape of Distributions

- Let's explore data and describe distributions.

4.1: Which One Doesn't Belong: Distribution Shape

Which one doesn't belong?

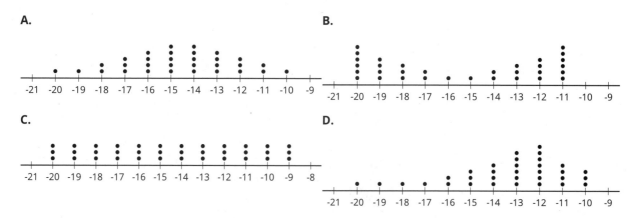

A.

B.

C.

D.

4.2: Matching Distributions

Take turns with your partner matching 2 different data displays that represent the distribution of the same set of data.

1. For each set that you find, explain to your partner how you know it's a match.

2. For each set that your partner finds, listen carefully to their explanation. If you disagree, discuss your thinking and work to reach an agreement.

3. When finished with all ten matches, describe the shape of each distribution.

4.3: Where Did The Distribution Come From?

Your teacher will assign you some of the matched distributions. Using the information provided in the data displays, make an educated guess about the survey question that produced this data. Be prepared to share your reasoning.

Are you ready for more?

This distribution shows the length in inches of fish caught and released from a nearby lake.

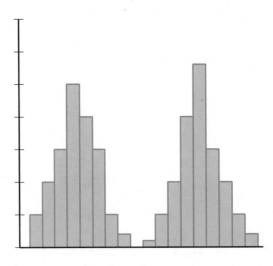

length of fish (inches)

1. Describe the shape of the distribution.

2. Make an educated guess about what could cause the distribution to have this shape.

Lesson 4 Summary

We can describe the shape of distributions as *symmetric, skewed, bell-shaped, bimodal,* or *uniform*. Here is a dot plot, histogram, and box plot representing the distribution of the same data set. This data set has a symmetric distribution.

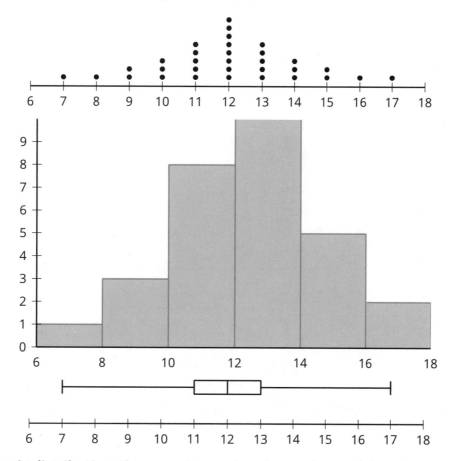

In a **symmetric distribution**, the mean is equal to the median and there is a vertical line of symmetry in the center of the data display. The histogram and the box plot both group data together. Since histograms and box plots do not display each data value individually, they do not provide information about the shape of the distribution to the same level of detail that a dot plot does. This distribution, in particular, can also be called bell-shaped. A **bell-shaped distribution** has a dot plot that takes the form of a bell with most of the data clustered near the center and fewer points farther from the center. This makes the measure of center a very good description of the data as a whole. Bell-shaped distributions are always symmetric or close to it.

Here is a dot plot, histogram, and box plot representing a skewed distribution.

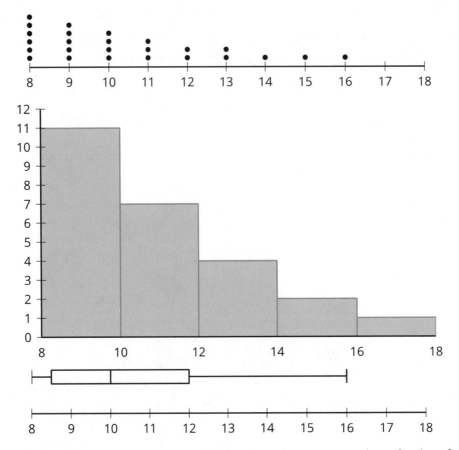

In a **skewed distribution**, one side of the distribution has more values farther from the bulk of the data than the other side. This results in the mean and median not being equal. In this skewed distribution, the data is skewed to the right because most of the data is near the 8 to 10 interval, but there are many points to the right. The mean is greater than the median. The large data values to the right cause the mean to shift in that direction while the median remains with the bulk of the data, so the mean is greater than the median for distributions that are skewed to the right. In a data set that is skewed to the left, a similar effect happens but to the other side. Again, the dot plot provides a greater level of detail about the shape of the distribution than either the histogram or the dot plot.

A **uniform distribution** has the data values evenly distributed throughout the range of the data. This causes the distribution to look like a rectangle.

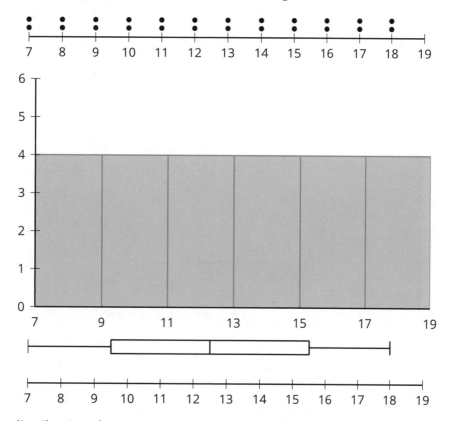

In a uniform distribution the mean is equal to the median since a uniform distribution is also a symmetric distribution. The box plot does not provide enough information to describe the shape of the distribution as uniform, though the even length of each quarter does suggest that the distribution may be approximately symmetric.

A **bimodal distribution** has two very common data values seen in a dot plot or histogram as distinct peaks.

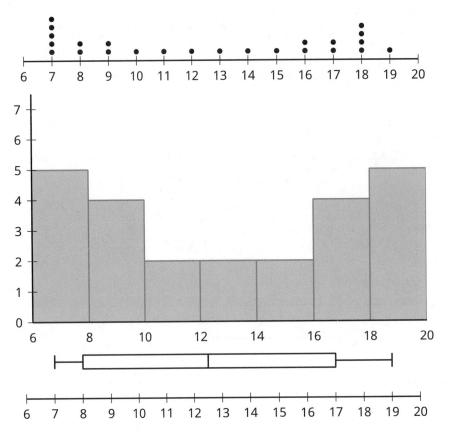

Sometimes, a bimodal distribution has most of the data clustered in the middle of the distribution. In these cases the center of the distribution does not describe the data very well. Bimodal distributions are not always symmetric. For example, the peaks may not be equally spaced from the middle of the distribution or other data values may disrupt the symmetry.

Glossary

- bell-shaped distribution
- bimodal distribution
- skewed distribution
- symmetric distribution
- uniform distribution

4. The data represent the number of ounces of water that 26 students drank before donating blood: 8, 8, 8, 16, 16, 16, 32, 32, 32, 32, 32, 32, 64, 64, 64, 64, 64, 64, 64, 80, 80, 80, 80, 88, 88, 88.

    a. Create a dot plot for the data.

    b. Create a box plot for the data.

    c. What information about the data is provided by the box plot that is not provided by the dot plot?

    d. What information about the data is provided by the dot plot that is not provided by the box plot?

    e. It was recommended that students drink 48 or more ounces of water. How could you use a histogram to easily display the number of students who drank the recommended amount?

(From Unit 1, Lesson 3.)

5. The box plot represents the distribution of the number of points scored by a cross country team at 12 meets.

22 24 26 28 30 32 34 36 38 40 42
points

a. If possible, find the mean. If not possible, explain why not.

b. If possible, find the median. If not possible, explain why not.

c. Did the cross country team ever score 30 points at a meet?

(From Unit 1, Lesson 2.)

Lesson 5: Calculating Measures of Center and Variability

- Let's calculate measures of center and measures of variability and know which are most appropriate for the data.

5.1: Calculating Centers

Decide if each situation is true or false. Explain your reasoning.

1. The mean can be found by adding all the numbers in a data set and dividing by the number of numbers in the data set.

2. The mean of the data in the dot plot is 4.

3. The median of the data set is 9 for the data: 4, 5, 9, 1, 10.

4. The median of the data in the dot plot is 3.5.

5.2: Heartbeats: Part 1

The heart rates of eight high school students are listed in beats per minute:

| 72 | 75 | 81 | 76 | 76 | 77 | 79 | 78 |

1. What is the interquartile range?

2. How many values in the data set are:
    a. less than Q1?

    b. between Q1 and the median?

    c. between the median and Q3?

    d. greater than Q3?

3. A pod of dolphins contains 800 dolphins of various ages and lengths. The median length of dolphins in this pod is 5.8 feet. What information does this tell you about the length of dolphins in this pod?

4. The same vocabulary test with 50 questions is given to 600 students from fifth to tenth grades and the number of correct responses is collected for each student in this group. The interquartile range is 40 correct responses. What information does this tell you about the number of correct responses for students taking this test?

5.3: Heartbeats: Part 2

1. Calculate the MAD using the same data from the previous activity by finding the average distance from each data value to the mean. You may find it helpful to organize your work by completing the table provided.

data values	mean	deviation from mean (data value - mean)	absolute deviation |deviation|
72			
75			
81			
76			
76			
77			
79			
78			

MAD:

2. For another data set, all of the values are either 3 beats per minute above the mean or 3 beats per minute below the mean. Is that enough information to find the MAD for this data set? If so, find the MAD. If not, what other information is needed? Explain your reasoning.

3. Several pennies are placed along a meter stick and the position in centimeters of each penny is recorded. The mean position is the 50 centimeter mark and the MAD is 10 centimeters. What information does this tell you about the position of the pennies along the meter stick?

Are you ready for more?

Suppose there are 6 pennies on a meter stick so that the mean position is the 50 centimeter mark and the MAD is 10 centimeters.

    1. Find possible locations for the 6 pennies.

    2. Find a different set of possible locations for the 6 pennies.

Lesson 5 Summary

The *mean absolute deviation*, or MAD, and the *interquartile range*, or IQR, are measures of variability. Measures of variability tell you how much the values in a data set tend to differ from one another. A greater measure of variability means that the data is more spread out while a smaller measure of variability means that the data is more consistent and close to the measure of center.

To calculate the MAD of a data set:

    1. Find the mean of the values in the data set.

    2. Find the distance between each data value and the mean on the number line:
$$|\text{data value} - \text{mean}|$$

    3. Find the mean of the distances. This value is the MAD.

To calculate the IQR, subtract the value of the first quartile from the value of the third quartile. Recall that the first and third quartile are included in the five number summary.

Lesson 5 Practice Problems

1. The data set represents the number of errors on a typing test.

   | 5 | 6 | 8 | 8 | 9 | 9 | 10 | 10 |

   10   12

   a. What is the median? Interpret this value in the situation.

   b. What is the IQR?

2. The data set represents the heights, in centimeters, of ten model bridges made for an engineering competition.

   | 13 | 14 | 14 | 16 | 16 | 16 | 16 | 18 |

   18   19

   a. What is the mean?

   b. What is the MAD?

3. Describe the shape of the distribution shown in the dot plot. The dot plot displays the golf scores from a golf tournament.

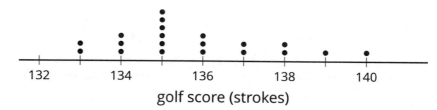

golf score (strokes)

(From Unit 1, Lesson 4.)

Algebra 1

39

4. The dot plot shows the weight, in grams, of several different rocks. Select **all** the terms that describe the shape of the distribution.

weight (grams)

A. bell-shaped

B. bimodal

C. skewed

D. symmetric

E. uniform

(From Unit 1, Lesson 4.)

5. The dot plot represents the distribution of wages earned during a one-week period by 12 college students.

weekly wages (dollars)

a. What is the mean? Interpret this value based on the situation.

b. What is the median? Interpret this value based on the situation.

c. Would a box plot of the same data have allowed you to find both the mean and the median?

(From Unit 1, Lesson 3.)

6. The box plot displays the temperature of saunas in degrees Fahrenheit. What is the median?

110 112 114 116 118 120 122 124 126

degrees (Fahrenheit)

(From Unit 1, Lesson 2.)

Algebra 1 iM KH

Lesson 6: Mystery Computations

Let's explore spreadsheets.

6.1: Make 24

Your teacher will give you 4 numbers. Use these numbers, along with mathematical operations like addition and multiplication, to make 24.

6.2: Mystery Operations

Navigate to this activity in the digital version of the materials or to ggbm.at/fjcybyqf.

Input different numbers in column A, and try to predict what will happen in column B. (Do not change anything in column B.)

1. How is the number in cell B2 related to all or some of the numbers in cells A2, A3, A4, and A5?

2. How is the number in cell B3 related to all or some of the numbers in cells A2, A3, A4, and A5?

3. How is the number in cell B4 related to all or some of the numbers in cells A2, A3, A4, and A5?

4. How is the number in cell B5 related to all or some of the numbers in cells A2, A3, A4, and A5?

Are you ready for more?

Check your conjectures by entering different kinds of numbers in column A, for example: fractions, decimals, very large numbers.

6.3: More Spreadsheets!

Navigate to this activity in the digital version of the materials or to ggbm.at/wu9t7kkd.

1. Change the spreadsheet so that B2 contains =A2+A4. To edit the formula in B2, you may have to click it twice.

2. Change the numbers in A2 through A5. Make sure that your new formula does what it is supposed to do by doing a mental calculation and checking the result in B2.

3. Change the contents of B3 so that B3 does something different.

4. Before trading with a partner, make sure your new formula is not visible by clicking in a different cell.

5. Trade with your partner.

6. Change the numbers in Column A to try and figure out your partner's new rule.

Lesson 6 Summary

Spreadsheets are useful mathematical and statistical tools. Here is an example of a spreadsheet. Each cell in the spreadsheet can be named with its column and row. For example, cell B2 contains the value 99. Cell A4 contains the value -17. Cell D1 is selected.

	A	B	C	D	E
1					
2		99			
3					
4	-17				
5				0.25	
6					
7					

Algebra 1 iM KH

It is possible for the value in a cell to depend on the value in other cells. Let's type the formula $= B2 - D5$ into cell D1.

	A	B	C	D	E
1				=B2-D5	
2		99			
3					
4	-17				
5				0.25	
6					
7					

When we press enter, D1 will display the result of subtracting the number in cell D5 from the number in cell B2.

	A	B	C	D	E
1				98.75	
2		99			
3					
4	-17				
5				0.25	
6					
7					

If we type new numbers into B2 or D5, the number in D1 will automatically change.

	A	B	C	D	E
1				79	
2		99			
3					
4	-17				
5				20	
6					
7					

Lesson 6 Practice Problems

1. What could be the formula used to compute the value shown in cell B3?

	A	B
1	change these	what happens here?
2	7	20
3	0	350
4	13	0
5	50	69
6	-1	

A. = B3 * B4

B. = A2 + A5

C. = A2 * A5

D. = Sum(A2:A6)

2. What number will appear in cell B2 when the user presses Enter?

	A	B
1	change these	what happens here?
2	10	=Sum(A3:A5)
3	5	
4	0	
5	-7	

3. Select **all** the formulas that could be used to calculate the value in cell B4.

	A	B
1	change these	what happens here?
2	7	20
3	0	350
4	13	0
5	50	69
6	-1	

A. =Product(A2:A6)

B. =Sum(A2:A6)

C. = A2 + A3

D. = A2 * A3

E. = A3 * A4 * A5

F. = A3 + A4 + A5

4. The formula in cell B2 is = Product(A2 : A5). Describe a way to change the contents of column A so that the value in cell B2 becomes -70.

	A	B
1	change these	what happens here?
2	10	0
3	5	
4	0	
5	-7	

5. The dot plot displays the number of books read by students during the semester.

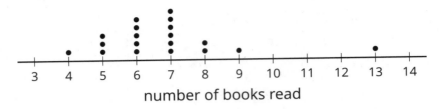

number of books read

   a. Which measure of center would you use given the shape of the distribution in the dot plot? Explain your reasoning.

   b. Which measure of variability would you use? Explain your reasoning.

(From Unit 1, Lesson 5.)

6. The dot plot displays the number of families living in different blocks of a town.

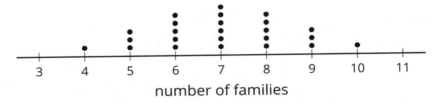

number of families

   a. Which measure of center would you use, given the shape of the distribution in the dot plot? Explain your reasoning.

   b. Which measure of variability would you use? Explain your reasoning.

(From Unit 1, Lesson 5.)

Algebra 1 iM KH

Lesson 7: Spreadsheet Computations

Let's use spreadsheets as calculators.

7.1: Dust Off Those Cobwebs

1. A person walks 4 miles per hour for 2.5 hours. How far do they walk?

2. A rectangle has an area of 24 square centimeters. What could be its length and width?

3. What is the area of this triangle?

7.2: A Spreadsheet Is a Calculator

Use a spreadsheet to compute each of the following. Type each computation in a new cell, instead of erasing a previous computation.

- $2 + 7$
- $2 - 7$
- $7 \cdot 2$
- 7^2
- $7 \div 2$

- $\frac{1}{7}$ of 91
- $0.1 \cdot 2 + 3$
- $0.1(2 + 3)$
- $13 \div \frac{1}{7}$
- The average of 2, 7, 8, and 11

7.3: Use the Contents of a Cell in a Calculation

1. Type any number in cell A1, and another number in cell A2. Then in cell A3, type =A1+A2. What happens?

2. In cell A4, compute the product of the numbers in A1 and A2.

3. In cell A5, compute the number in A1 raised to the power of the number in A2.

4. Now, type a new number in cell A1. What happens?

5. Type a new number in cell A2. What happens?

6. Use nearby cells to label the contents of each cell. For example in cell B3, type "the sum of A1 and A2." (This is a good habit to get into. It will remind you and anyone else using the spreadsheet what each cell means.)

7.4: Solve Some Problems

For each problem:

- Estimate the answer before calculating anything.

- Use the spreadsheet to calculate the answer.

- Write down the answer and the formula you used in the spreadsheet to calculate it.

1. The speed limit on a highway is 110 kilometers per hour. How much time does it take a car to travel 132 kilometers at this speed?

2. In a right triangle, the lengths of the sides that make a right angle are 98.7 cm and 24.6 cm. What is the area of the triangle?

3. A recipe for fruit punch uses 2 cups of seltzer water, $\frac{1}{4}$ cup of pineapple juice, and $\frac{2}{3}$ cup of cranberry juice. How many cups of fruit punch are in 5 batches of this recipe?

4. Check in with a partner and resolve any discrepancies with your answer to the last question. Next, type 2, $\frac{1}{4}$, $\frac{2}{3}$, and 5 in separate cells. (You may find it helpful to label cells next to them with the meaning of each number.) In a blank cell, type a formula for the total amount of fruit punch that uses the values in the other four cells. Now you should be able to easily figure out:

a. How much in 7.25 batches?

b. How much in 5 batches if you change the recipe to 1.5 cups of seltzer water per batch?

c. Change the ratio of the ingredients in the fruit punch so that you would like the flavor. How many total cups are in $\frac{1}{2}$ batch?

Lesson 7 Summary

A spreadsheet can be thought of as a type of calculator. For example, in a cell, you could type $= 2 + 3$, and then the sum of 5 is displayed in the cell. You can also perform operations on the values in other cells. For example, if you type a number in A1 and a number in A2, and then in A3 type $= A1 + A2$, then A3 will display the sum of the values in cells A1 and A2.

Famliarize yourself with how your spreadsheet software works on your device..

- On some spreadsheet programs, an = symbol must be typed before the expression in the cell. (On others, it does not matter if your expression begins with =.)

- Know how to "submit" the expression so the computation takes place. If your device has a keyboard, it's likely the enter key. On a touchscreen device, you may have to tap a check mark.

- Learn symbols to use for various operations, and how to find them on your keyboard. Here are the symbols used for some typical operations:
    - + for add

    - - for subtract or for a negative number (this symbol does double duty in most spreadsheets)

    - * for multiply

    - / for divide

    - a / b for the fraction $\frac{a}{b}$

    - ^ for exponent

    - . for a decimal point

    - ( ) to tell it what to compute first. (often needed around fractions)

Algebra 1 iM KH

Lesson 7 Practice Problems

1. Write a formula you could type into a spreadsheet to compute the value of each expression.

   a. $(19.2) \cdot 73$

   b. 1.1^5

   c. $2.34 \div 5$

   d. $\frac{91}{7}$

2. A long-distance runner jogs at a constant speed of 7 miles per hour for 45 minutes. Which spreadsheet formula would give the distance she traveled?

   A. = 7 * 45

   B. = 7 / 45

   C. = 7 * (3 / 4)

   D. = 7 / (3 / 4)

3. In a right triangle, the lengths of the sides that make a right angle are 3.4 meters and 5.6 meters. Select **all** the spreadsheet formulas that would give the area of this triangle.

   A. = 3.4 * 5.6

   B. = 3.4 * 5.6 * 2

   C. = 3.4 * 5.6 / 2

   D. = 3.4 * 5.6 * (1/2)

   E. = (3.4 * 5.6) / 2

4. This spreadsheet should compute the total ounces of sparkling grape juice based on the number of batches, ounces of grape juice in a single batch, and ounces of sparkling water in a single batch.

	A	B
1	number of batches	4
2	ounces of grape juice in 1 batch	3
3	ounces of sparkling water in 1 batch	7
4	total ounces	

a. Write a formula for cell B4 that uses the values in cells B1, B2, and B3, to compute the total ounces of sparkling grape juice.

b. How would the output of the formula change if the value in cell B1 was changed to 10?

c. What would change about the sparkling grape juice if the value in B3 was changed to 10?

5. The dot plot and the box plot represent the same distribution of data.

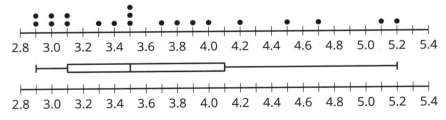

a. How does the median change when the highest value, 5.2, is removed?

b. How does the IQR change when the highest value, 5.2, is removed?

(From Unit 1, Lesson 5.)

Algebra 1 iM KH

6. Describe the shape of the distribution shown in the histogram which displays the light output, in lumens, of various light sources.

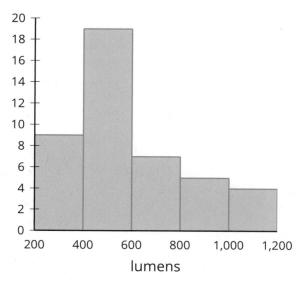

(From Unit 1, Lesson 4.)

7. The dot plot represents the distribution of the number of goals scored by a soccer team in 10 games.

goals scored

a. If possible, find the mean. If not possible, explain why not.

b. If possible, find the median. If not possible, explain why not.

c. Did the soccer team ever score exactly 3 goals in one of the games?

(From Unit 1, Lesson 2.)

Lesson 8: Spreadsheet Shortcuts

Let's explore recursive formulas in spreadsheets.

8.1: Tables of Equivalent Ratios

Here is a table of equivalent ratios:

a	b
3	15
10	50
6	30
1	
	80

1. Complete the table with the missing values.

2. Explain what it means to say that the pairs of numbers are equivalent ratios.

8.2: The Birthday Trick

Navigate to this activity in the digital version of the materials or to ggbm.at/djcz6fjf.

1. In cell B4, we want to enter = B1 * 5 to multiply the month by 5. Enter this, but when you are about to type B1, instead, click on cell B1. This shortcut can be used any time: click on a cell instead of typing its address.

2. Practice this technique as you program each cell in B5 through B10 to perform the right computation.

3. When you are finished, does cell B10 show a number that contains the month and day of your birthday? If not, troubleshoot your computations.

4. Try changing the month and day in cells B1 and B2. The rest of the computations should automatically update. If not, troubleshoot your computations.

Are you ready for more?

Why does this trick work? Try using m for the month and d for the day, and writing the entire computation as an algebraic expression. Can you see why the resulting number contains the month and day?

8.3: Using Spreadsheet Patterns

Navigate to this activity in the digital version of the materials or to the URL, ggbm.at/wu9t7kkd.

The spreadsheet contains a table of equivalent ratios.

1. Use spreadsheet calculations to continue the pattern in columns A and B, down to row 5. Pause for discussion.

2. Click on cell A5. See the tiny blue square in the bottom right corner of the cell? Click it and drag it down for several cells and let go.

3. Repeat this, starting with cell B5.

Lesson 8 Summary

Sometimes you want to create a list of numbers based on a rule. For example, let's say that the cost of a gym membership is a $25 sign-up fee followed by monthly dues of $35. We may want to know how much the membership will cost over the course of 6 months. We could use a spreadsheet and set it up this way:

	A	B	C
1	sign-up fee	25	
2	total cost after 1 month	=B1+35	
3	total cost after 2 months		
4	total cost after 3 months		
5	total cost after 4 months		
6	total cost after 5 months		
7	total cost after 6 months		
8			
9			

Which results in:

	A	B	C
1	sign-up fee	25	
2	total cost after 1 month	60	
3	total cost after 2 months		
4	total cost after 3 months		
5	total cost after 4 months		
6	total cost after 5 months		
7	total cost after 6 months		
8			
9			

Algebra 1 iM KH

See the little square on the lower-right corner of cell B2? If we click and drag that down, it will keep adding 35 to the value above to find the value in the next row. Drag it down far enough, and we can see the total cost after 6 months.

	A	B	C
1	sign-up fee	25	
2	total cost after 1 month	60	
3	total cost after 2 months	95	
4	total cost after 3 months	130	
5	total cost after 4 months	165	
6	total cost after 5 months	200	
7	total cost after 6 months	235	
8			
9			

Any time you need to repeat a mathematical operation several times, continuing a pattern by dragging in a spreadsheet might be a good choice.

Lesson 8 Practice Problems

1. *Technology required.* Open a blank spreadsheet. Use "fill down" to recreate this table of equivalent ratios. You should not need to type anything in rows 3–10.

	A	B
1	3	7
2	6	14
3	9	21
4	12	28
5	15	35
6	18	42
7	21	49
8	24	56
9	27	63
10	30	70

2. A list of numbers is made with the pattern: Start with 11, and subtract 4 to find the next number.

   Here is the beginning of the list: 11, 7, 3, . . .

   Explain how you could use "fill down" in a spreadsheet to find the tenth number in this list. (You do *not* need to actually find this number.)

3. Here is a spreadsheet showing the computations for a different version of the birthday trick:

	A	B
1	month	7
2	day	4
3		
4	multiply month by 50	
5	add 30	
6	multiply by 2	
7	add the day	
8	subtract 60	
9		
10		

Explain what formulas you would enter is cells B4 through B8 so that cell B8 shows a number representing the month and day. (In this example, cell B8 should show 704.) If you have access to a spreadsheet, try your formulas with a month and day to see whether it works.

4. Write a formula you could type into a spreadsheet to compute the value of each expression.

   a. $\frac{2}{5}$ of 35

   b. $25 \div \frac{5}{3}$

   c. $\left(\frac{1}{11}\right)^4$

   d. The average of 0, 3, and 17

   (From Unit 1, Lesson 7.)

5. The data set represents the number of cars in a town given a speeding ticket each day for 10 days.

| 2 | 4 | 5 | 5 | 7 | 7 | 8 | 8 |

| 8 | 12 |

a. What is the median? Interpret this value in the situation.

b. What is the IQR?

(From Unit 1, Lesson 5.)

6. The data set represents the most recent sale price, in thousands of dollars, of ten homes on a street.

| 85 | 91 | 93 | 99 | 99 | 99 | 102 | 108 |

| 110 | 115 |

a. What is the mean?

b. What is the MAD?

(From Unit 1, Lesson 5.)

Algebra 1 iM **KH**

Lesson 9: Technological Graphing

- Let's use technology to represent data.

9.1: It Begins With Data

Open a spreadsheet window and enter the data so that each value is in its own cell in column A.

1. How many values are in the spreadsheet? Explain your reasoning.

2. If you entered the data in the order that the values are listed, the number 7 is in the cell at position A1 and the number 5 is in cell A5. List all of the cells that contain the number 13.

3. In cell C1 type the word "Sum", in C2 type "Mean", and in C3 type "Median". You may wish to double-click or drag the vertical line between columns C and D to allow the entire words to be seen.

	A
1	7
2	8
3	4
4	13
5	5
6	15
7	14
8	8
9	12
10	2

	A
11	8
12	13
13	12
14	13
15	6
16	1
17	9
18	4
19	9
20	15

9.2: Finding Spreadsheet Statistics

Using the data from the warm-up, we can calculate a few **statistics** and look at the data.

- Next to the word Sum, in cell D1, type =Sum(A1:A20)

- Next to the word Mean, in cell D2, type =Mean(A1:A20)

- Next to the word Median, in cell D3, type =Median(A1:A20)

1. What are the values for each of the statistics?

2. Change the value in A1 to 8. How does that change the statistics?

3. What value can be put into A1 to change the mean to 10.05 and the median to 9?

We can also use Geogebra to create data displays.

- Click on the letter A for the first column so that the entire column is highlighted.

- Click on the button that looks like a histogram to get a new window labeled One Variable Analysis .

- Click Analyze to see a histogram of the data.

1. Click the button Σx to see many of the statistics.
   a. What does the value for n represent?

   b. What does the value for Σx represent?

   c. What other statistics do you recognize?

2. Adjust the slider next to the word Histogram. What changes?

3. Click on the button to the right of the slider to bring in another window with more options. Then, click the box next to Set Classes Manually and set the Width to 5. What does this do to the histogram?

4. Click the word Histogram and look at a box plot and dot plot of the data. When looking at the box plot, notice there is an x on the right side of box plot. This represents a data point that is considered an outlier. Click on the button to the right of the slider and uncheck the box labeled Show Outliers to include this point in the box plot. What changes? Why might you want to show outliers? Why might you want to include or exclude outliers?

9.3: Making Digital Displays

Use the data you collected from the numerical, statistical question from a previous lesson. Use technology to create a dot plot, boxplot, and histogram for your data. Then find the mean, median, and interquartile range for the data.

Are you ready for more?

A stem and leaf plot is a table where each data point is indicated by writing the first digit(s) on the left (the stem) and the last digit(s) on the right (the leaves). Each stem is written only once and shared by all data points with the same first digit(s). For example, the values 31, 32, and 45 might be represented like:

$$
\begin{array}{c|cc}
3 & 1 & 2 \\
4 & 5 &
\end{array}
$$

Key: 3 | 1 means 31

A class took an exam and earned the scores:

86, 73, 85, 86, 72, 94, 88, 98, 87, 86, 85, 93, 75, 64, 82, 95, 99, 76, 84, 68

1. Use technology to create a stem and leaf plot for this data set.

2. How can we see the shape of the distribution from this plot?

3. What information can we see from a stem and leaf plot that we cannot see from a histogram?

4. What do we have more control of in a histogram than in a stem and leaf plot?

Lesson 9 Summary

Data displays (like histograms or box plots) are very useful for quickly understanding a large amount of information, but often take a long time to construct accurately using pencil and paper. Technology can help create these displays as well as calculate useful *statistics* much faster than doing the same tasks by hand. Especially with very large data sets (in some experiments, millions of pieces of data are collected), technology is essential for putting the information into forms that are more easily understood.

A **statistic** is a quantity that is calculated from sample data as a measure of a distribution. *Mean* and *median* are examples of statistics that are measures of center. *Mean absolute deviation (MAD)* and *interquartile range (IQR)* are examples of statistics that are measures of variability. Although the interpretation must still be done by people, using the tools available can improve the accuracy and speed of doing computations and creating graphs.

Glossary

- statistic

Lesson 9 Practice Problems

1. *Technology required.* The data represent the average customer ratings for several items sold online.

0.5	1	1.2	1.3	2.1	2.1	2.1	2.3
2.5	2.6	3.5	3.6	3.7	4	4.1	4.1
4.2	4.2	4.5	4.7	4.8			

   a. Use technology to create a histogram for the data with intervals 0–1, 1–2, and so on.

   b. Describe the shape of the distribution.

   c. Which interval has the highest frequency?

2. *Technology required.* The data represent the amount of corn, in bushels per acre, harvested from different locations.

   133, 133, 134, 134, 134, 135, 135, 135, 135, 135, 135, 136, 136, 136, 137, 137, 138, 138, 139, 140

   a. Use technology to create a dot plot and a box plot.

   b. What is the shape of the distribution?

   c. Compare the information displayed by the dot plot and box plot.

3. a. Describe the shape of the distribution.

   b. How many values are represented by the histogram?

   c. Write a statistical question that could have produced the data set summarized in the histogram.

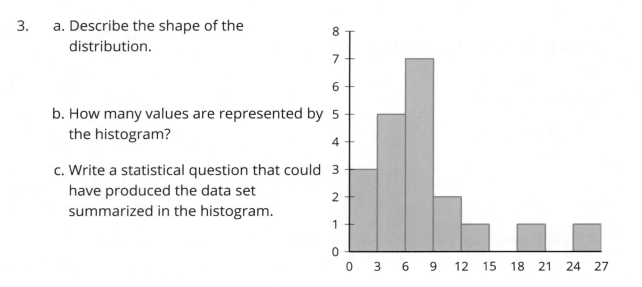

(From Unit 1, Lesson 4.)

4. The dot plot represents the distribution of satisfaction ratings for a landscaping company on a scale of 1 to 10. Twenty-five customers were surveyed.

satisfaction ratings

On average, what was the satisfaction rating of the landscaping company?

(From Unit 1, Lesson 3.)

Lesson 10: The Effect of Extremes

- Let's see how statistics change with the data.

10.1: Battle Royale

Several video games are based on a genre called "Battle Royale" in which 100 players are on an island and they fight until only 1 player remains and is crowned the winner. This type of game can often be played in solo mode as individuals or in team mode in groups of 2.

1. What information would you use to determine the top players in each mode (solo and team)? Explain your reasoning.

2. One person claims that the best solo players play game A. Another person claims that game B has better solo players. How could you display data to help inform their discussion? Explain your reasoning.

10.2: Separated by Skew

1. Use technology to create a dot plot that represents the distribution of the data, then describe the shape of the distribution.

6	7	8	8	9	9	9	10
10	10	10	11	11	11	12	12
13	14						

2. Find the mean and median of the data.

3. Find the mean and median of the data with 2 additional values included as described.

   a. Add 2 values to the original data set that are greater than 14.

   b. Add 2 values to the original data set that are less than 6.

   c. Add 1 value that is greater than 14 and 1 value that is less than 6 to the original data set.

   d. Add the two values, 50 and 100, to the original data set.

4. Share your work with your group. What do you notice is happening with the mean and median based on the additional values?

5. Change the values so that the distribution fits the description given to you by your teacher, then find the mean and median.

6. Find another group that created a distribution with a different description. Explain your work and listen to their explanation, then compare your measures of center.

10.3: Plots Matching Measures

Create a possible dot plot with at least 10 values for each of the conditions listed. Each dot plot must have at least 3 values that are different.

1. a distribution that has both mean and median of 10

2. a distribution that has both mean and median of -15

3. a distribution that has a median of 2.5 and a mean greater than the median

4. a distribution that has a median of 5 and a median greater than the mean

Are you ready for more?

The mean and the median are by far the most common measures of center for numerical data. There are other measures of center, though, that are sometimes used. For each measure of center, list some possible advantages and disadvantages. Be sure to consider how it is affected by extremes.

1. *Interquartile mean*: The mean of only those points between the first quartile and the third quartile.

2. *Midhinge*: The mean of the first quartile and the third quartile.

3. *Midrange*: The mean of the minimum and maximum value.

4. *Trimean:* The mean of the first quartile, the median, the median again, and the third quartile. So we are averaging four numbers as the median is counted twice.

Lesson 10 Summary

Is it better to use the mean or median to describe the center of a data set?

The mean gives equal importance to each value when finding the center. The mean usually represents the typical values well when the data has a symmetric distribution. On the other hand, the mean can be greatly affected by changes to even a single value.

The median tells you the middle value in the data set, so changes to a single value usually do not affect the median much. So, the median is more appropriate for data that is not very symmetric.

We can look at the distribution of a data set and draw conclusions about the mean and the median.

Here is a dot plot showing the amount of time a dart takes to hit a target in seconds. The data produces a symmetric distribution.

time to hit dartboard in seconds

When a distribution is symmetric, the median and mean are both found in the middle of the distribution. Since the median is the middle value (or mean of the two middle values) of a data set, you can use the symmetry around the center of a symmetric distribution to find it easily. For the mean, you need to know that the sum of the distances away from the mean of the values greater than the mean is equal to the sum of the distances away from the mean of the values less than the mean. Using the symmetry of the symmetric distribution you can see that there are four values 0.1 second above the mean, two values 0.2 seconds above the mean, one value 0.3 seconds above the mean, and one value 0.4 seconds above the mean. Likewise, you can see that there are the same number of values the same distances below the mean.

Here is a dot plot using the same data, but with two of the values changed, resulting in a skewed distribution.

time to hit dartboard in seconds

When you have a skewed distribution, the distribution is not symmetric, so you are not able to use the symmetry to find the median and the mean. The median is still 1.4 seconds since it is still the middle value. The mean, on the other hand, is now about 1.273 seconds. The mean is less than the median because the lower values (0.3 and 0.4) result in a smaller value for the mean.

The median is usually more resistant to extreme values than the mean. For this reason, the median is the preferred measure of center when a distribution is skewed or if there are extreme values. When using the median, you would also use the IQR as the preferred measure of variability. In a more symmetric distribution, the mean is the preferred measure of center and the MAD is the preferred measure of variability.

Lesson 10 Practice Problems

1. Select **all** the distribution shapes for which it is most often appropriate to use the mean.

    A. bell-shaped

    B. bimodal

    C. skewed

    D. symmetric

    E. uniform

2. For which distribution shape is it usually appropriate to use the median when summarizing the data?

    A. bell-shaped

    B. skewed

    C. symmetric

    D. uniform

3. The number of writing instruments in some teachers' desks is displayed in the dot plot. Which is greater, the mean or the median? Explain your reasoning using the shape of the distribution.

number of writing instruments

4. A student has these scores on their assignments. The teacher is considering dropping a lowest score. What effect does eliminating the lowest value, 0, from the data set have on the mean and median?

0, 40, 60, 70, 75, 80, 85, 95, 95, 100

(From Unit 1, Lesson 9.)

5.   a. What is the five-number summary for the data 2, 2, 4, 4, 5, 5, 6, 7, 9, 15?

       b. When the maximum, 15, is removed from the data set, what is the five-number summary?

(From Unit 1, Lesson 9.)

6. The box plot summarizes the test scores for 100 students:

55 60 65 70 75 80 85 90 95 100
test scores

Which term best describes the shape of the distribution?

   A. bell-shaped

   B. uniform

   C. skewed

   D. symmetric

(From Unit 1, Lesson 4.)

7. The histogram represents the distribution of lengths, in inches, of 25 catfish caught in a lake.

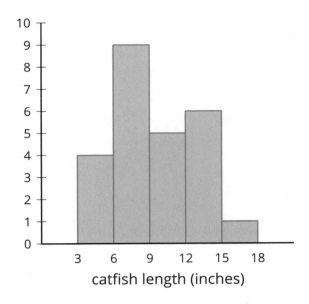

a. If possible, find the mean. If not possible, explain why not.

b. If possible, find the median. If not possible, explain why not.

c. Were any of the fish caught 12 inches long?

d. Were any of the fish caught 19 inches long?

(From Unit 1, Lesson 2.)

Lesson 11: Comparing and Contrasting Data Distributions

- Let's investigate variability using data displays and summary statistics.

11.1: Math Talk: Mean

Evaluate the mean of each data set mentally.

27, 30, 33

61, 71, 81, 91, 101

0, 100, 100, 100, 100

0, 5, 6, 7, 12

11.2: Describing Data Distributions

1. Your teacher will give you a set of cards. Take turns with your partner to match a data display with a written statement.
   a. For each match that you find, explain to your partner how you know it's a match.

   b. For each match that your partner finds, listen carefully to their explanation. If you disagree, discuss your thinking and work to reach an agreement.

2. After matching, determine if the mean or median is more appropriate for describing the center of the data set based on the distribution shape. Discuss your reasoning with your partner. If it is not given, calculate (if possible) or estimate the appropriate measure of center. Be prepared to explain your reasoning.

11.3: Visual Variability and Statistics

Each box plot summarizes the number of miles driven each day for 30 days in each month. The box plots represent, in order, the months of August, September, October, November, and December.

1. The five box plots have the same median. Explain why the median is more appropriate for describing the center of the data set than the mean for these distributions.

2. Arrange the box plots in order of least variability to greatest variability. Check with another group to see if they agree.

a.
miles driven each day in August

b.
miles driven each day in September

c.
miles driven each day in October

d.
miles driven each day in November

e.
miles driven each day in December

Algebra 1 iM KH

3. The five dot plots have the same mean. Explain why the mean is more appropriate for describing the center of the data set than the median.

4. Arrange the dot plots in order of least variability to greatest variability. Check with another group to see if they agree.

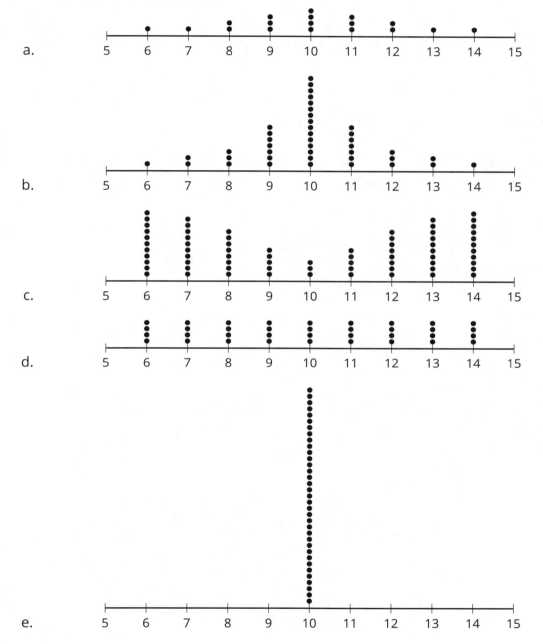

Are you ready for more?

1. These two box plots have the same median and the same IQR. How could we compare the variability of the two distributions?

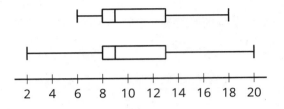

2. These two dot plots have the same mean and the same MAD. How could we compare the variability of the two distributions?

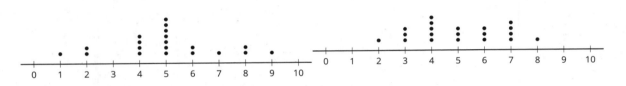

Lesson 11 Summary

The mean absolute deviation, or MAD, is a measure of variability that is calculated by finding the mean distance from the mean of all the data points. Here are two dot plots, each with a mean of 15 centimeters, displaying the length of sea scallop shells in centimeters.

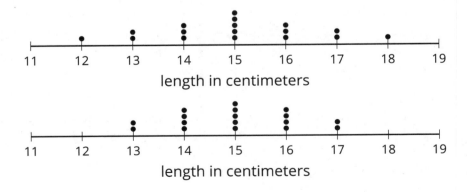

Algebra 1   iM KH

Notice that both dot plots show a symmetric distribution so the mean and the MAD are appropriate choices for describing center and variability. The data in the first dot plot appear to be more spread apart than the data in the second dot plot, so you can say that the first data set appears to have greater variability than the second data set. This is confirmed by the MAD. The MAD of the first data set is 1.18 centimeters and the MAD of the second data set is approximately 0.94 cm. This means that the values in the first data set are, on average, about 1.18 cm away from the mean and the values in the second data set are, on average, about 0.94 cm away from the mean. The greater the MAD of the data, the greater the variability of the data.

The interquartile range, IQR, is a measure of variability that is calculated by subtracting the value for the first quartile, Q1, from the value for the the third quartile, Q3. These two box plots represent the distributions of the lengths in centimeters of a different group of sea scallop shells, each with a median of 15 centimeters.

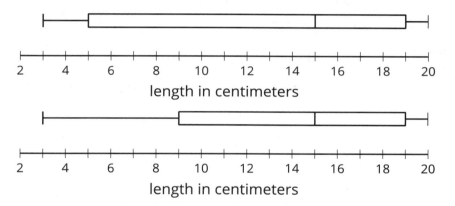

Notice that neither of the box plots have a symmetric distribution. The median and the IQR are appropriate choices for describing center and variability for these data sets. The middle half of the data displayed in the first box plot appear to be more spread apart, or show greater variability, than the middle half of the data displayed in the second box plot. The IQR of the first distribution is 14 cm and 9 cm for the second data set. The IQR measures the difference between the median of the second half of the data, Q3, and the median of the first half, Q1, of the data, so it is not impacted by the minimum or the maximum value in the data set. It is a measure of the spread of middle 50% of the data.

The MAD is calculated using every value in the data while the IQR is calculated using only the values for Q1 and Q3.

Lesson 11 Practice Problems

1. In science class, Clare and Lin estimate the mass of eight different objects that actually weigh 2,000 grams each.

   Some summary statistics:

   Clare

   - mean: 2,000 grams

   - MAD: 275 grams

   - median: 2,000 grams

   - IQR: 500 grams

   Lin

   - mean: 2,000 grams

   - MAD: 225 grams

   - median: 1,950 grams

   - IQR: 350 grams

   Which student was better at estimating the mass of the objects? Explain your reasoning.

2. A reporter counts the number of times a politician talks about jobs in their campaign speeches. What is the MAD of the data represented in the dot plot?

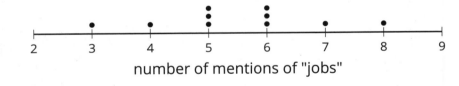

number of mentions of "jobs"

   A. 1.1 mentions

   B. 2 mentions

   C. 2.5 mentions

   D. 5.5 mentions

3. Four amateur miniature golfers attempt to finish 100 holes under par several times. Each round of 100, the number of holes they successfully complete under par is recorded. Due to the presence of extreme values, box plots were determined to be the best representation for the data. List the four box plots in order of variability from least to greatest.

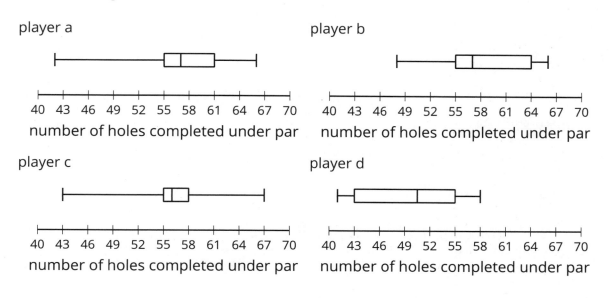

player a

number of holes completed under par

player b

number of holes completed under par

player c

number of holes completed under par

player d

number of holes completed under par

4. Select **all** the distribution shapes for which the median *could be* much less than the mean.

    A. symmetric

    B. bell-shaped

    C. skewed left

    D. skewed right

    E. bimodal

(From Unit 1, Lesson 10.)

Algebra 1

5.   a. What is the five-number summary for the data 0, 2, 2, 4, 5, 5, 5, 5, 7, 11?

      b. When the minimum, 0, is removed from the data set, what is the five-number
         summary?

(From Unit 1, Lesson 9.)

6. What effect does eliminating the highest value, 180, from the data set have on the
   mean and median?

   25, 50, 50, 60, 70, 85, 85, 90, 90, 180

(From Unit 1, Lesson 9.)

7. The histogram represents the distribution
   of the number of seconds it took for each
   of 50 students to find the answer to a
   trivia question using the internet. Which
   interval contains the median?

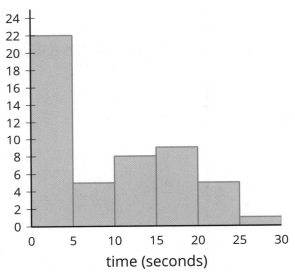

   A. 0 to 5 seconds

   B. 5 to 10 seconds

   C. 10 to 15 seconds

   D. 15 to 20 seconds

(From Unit 1, Lesson 3.)

Algebra 1 iM KH

Lesson 12: Standard Deviation

- Let's learn about standard deviation, another measure of variability.

12.1: Notice and Wonder: Measuring Variability

What do you notice? What do you wonder?

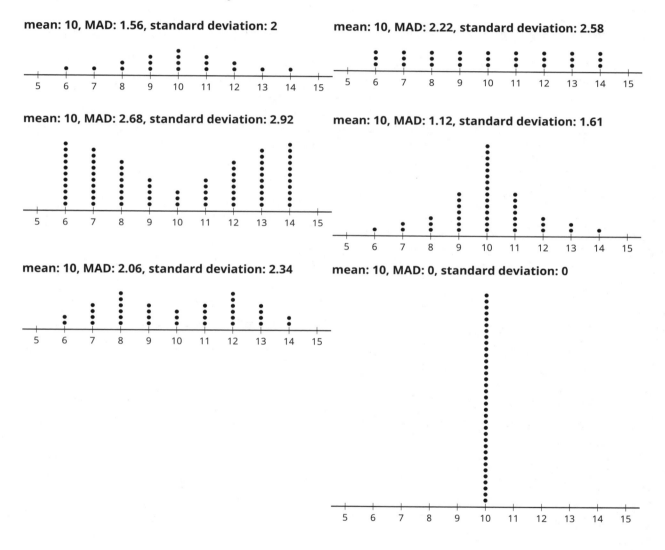

mean: 10, MAD: 1.56, standard deviation: 2

mean: 10, MAD: 2.22, standard deviation: 2.58

mean: 10, MAD: 2.68, standard deviation: 2.92

mean: 10, MAD: 1.12, standard deviation: 1.61

mean: 10, MAD: 2.06, standard deviation: 2.34

mean: 10, MAD: 0, standard deviation: 0

12.2: Investigating Standard Deviation

Use technology to find the mean and the standard deviation for the data in the dot plots.

1. What do you notice about the mean and standard deviation you and your partner found for the three dot plots?

2. Invent some data that fits the conditions. Be prepared to share your data set and reasoning for choice of values.

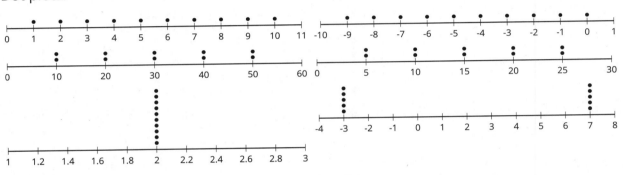

Partner 1

Dot plots:

Conditions:

- 10 numbers with a standard deviation equal to the standard deviation of your first dot plot with a mean of 6.

- 10 numbers with a standard deviation three times greater than the data in the first row.

- 10 different numbers with a standard deviation as close to 2 as you can get in 1 minute.

Partner 2

Dot plots:

Conditions:

- 10 numbers with a standard deviation equal to the standard deviation of your first dot plot with a mean of 12.

- 10 numbers with a standard deviation four times greater than the data in the first row.

- 10 different numbers with a standard deviation as close to 2 as you can get in 1 minute.

Algebra 1 iM KH

12.3: Investigating Variability

Begin with the data:

1, 2, 3, 4, 5, 6, 7, 8, 9, 10, 11, 12, 13, 14, 15, 16, 17, 18, 19, 20

1. Use technology to find the mean, standard deviation, median, and interquartile range.

2. How do the standard deviation and mean change when you remove the greatest value from the data set? How do they change if you add a value to the data set that is twice the greatest value?

3. What do you predict will happen to the standard deviation and mean when you remove the least value from the data set? Check to see if your prediction was correct.

4. What happens to the standard deviation and mean when you add a value to the data set equal to the mean? Add a second value equal to the mean. What happens?

5. Add, change, and remove values from the data set to answer the question: What appears to change more easily, the standard deviation or the interquartile range? Explain your reasoning.

Are you ready for more?

How is the standard deviation calculated? We have seen that the standard deviation behaves a lot like the mean absolute deviation and that is because the key idea behind both is the same.

1. Using the original data set, calculate the deviation of each point from the mean by subtracting the mean from each data point.

2. If we just tried to take a mean of those deviations what would we get?

3. There are two common ways to turn negative values into more useful positive values: take the absolute value or square the value. To find the MAD we find the absolute value of each deviation, then find the mean of those numbers. To find the standard deviation we square each of the deviations, then find the mean of those numbers. Then finally take the square root of that mean. Compute the MAD and the standard deviation of the original data set.

Lesson 12 Summary

We can describe the variability of a distribution using the **standard deviation**. The standard deviation is a measure of variability that is calculated using a method that is similar to the one used to calculate the MAD, or mean absolute deviation.

A deeper understanding of the importance of standard deviation as a measure of variability will come with a deeper study of statistics. For now, know that standard deviation is mathematically important and will be used as the appropriate measure of variability when mean is an appropriate measure of center.

Like the MAD, the standard deviation is large when the data set is more spread out, and the standard deviation is small when the variability is small. The intuition you gained about MAD will also work for the standard deviation.

Glossary

- standard deviation

Lesson 12 Practice Problems

1. The shoe size for all the pairs of shoes in a person's closet are recorded.

| 7 | 7 | 7 | 7 | 7 | 7 | 7 | 7 |

| 7 | 7 |

a. What is the mean?

b. What is the standard deviation?

2. Here is a data set:

| 1 | 2 | 3 | 3 | 4 | 4 | 4 | 4 |

| 5 | 5 | 6 | 7 |

a. What happens to the mean and standard deviation of the data set when the 7 is changed to a 70?

b. For the data set with the value of 70, why would the median be a better choice for the measure of center than the mean?

3. Which of these best estimates the standard deviation of points in a card game?

points in a card game

A. 5 points

B. 20 points

C. 50 points

D. 500 points

4. The mean of data set A is 43.5 and the MAD is 3.7. The mean of data set B is 12.8 and the MAD is 4.1.

   a. Which data set shows greater variability? Explain your reasoning.

   b. What differences would you expect to see when comparing the dot plots of the two data sets?

(From Unit 1, Lesson 11.)

5. Select **all** the distribution shapes for which the mean and median *must be* about the same.

   A. bell-shaped

   B. bimodal

   C. skewed

   D. symmetric

   E. uniform

(From Unit 1, Lesson 10.)

Algebra 1

6. What is the IQR?

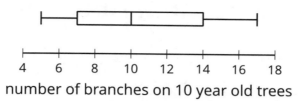

number of branches on 10 year old trees

   A. 5 branches

   B. 7 branches

   C. 10 branches

   D. 12 branches

(From Unit 1, Lesson 11.)

7. The data represent the number of cans collected by different classes for a service project.

12	14	22	14	18	23	42	13
9	19	22	14				

   a. Find the mean.

   b. Find the median.

   c. Eliminate the greatest value, 42, from the data set. Explain how the measures of center change.

(From Unit 1, Lesson 9.)

Lesson 13: More Standard Deviation

- Let's continue to interpret standard deviation.

13.1: Math Talk: Outlier Math

Evaluate mentally.

$0.5 \cdot 30$

$1.5 \cdot 30$

$100 - 1.5 \cdot 30$

$100 - 1.5 \cdot 18$

13.2: Info Gap: African and Asian Elephants

Your teacher will give you either a problem card or a data card. Do not show or read your card to your partner.

If your teacher gives you the data card:

1. Silently read the information on your card.
2. Ask your partner "What specific information do you need?" and wait for your partner to ask for information. Only give information that is on your card. (Do not figure out anything for your partner!)
3. Before telling your partner the information, ask "Why do you need to know (that piece of information)?"
4. Read the problem card, and solve the problem independently.
5. Share the data card, and discuss your reasoning.

If your teacher gives you the problem card:

1. Silently read your card and think about what information you need to answer the question.
2. Ask your partner for the specific information that you need.
3. Explain to your partner how you are using the information to solve the problem.
4. When you have enough information, share the problem card with your partner, and solve the problem independently.
5. Read the data card, and discuss your reasoning.

13.3: Interpreting Measures of Center and Variability

For each situation, you are given two graphs of data, a measure of center for each, and a measure of variability for each.

- Interpret the measure of center in terms of the situation.

- Interpret the measure of variability in terms of the situation.

- Compare the two data sets.

1. The heights of the 40 trees in each of two forests are collected.

mean: 44.8 feet, standard deviation: 4.72 feet

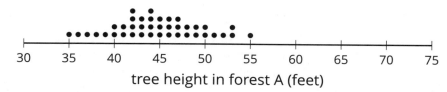

tree height in forest A (feet)

mean: 56.03 feet, standard deviation: 7.87 feet

tree height in forest B (feet)

2. The number of minutes it takes Lin and Noah to finish their tests in German class is collected for the year.

mean: 29.48 minutes, standard deviation: 5.44 minutes

time to finish test for Lin (min)

mean: 28.44 minutes, standard deviation: 7.40 minutes

time to finish test for Noah (min)

3. The number of raisins in a cereal with a name brand and the generic version of the same cereal are collected for several boxes.

mean: 289.1 raisins, standard deviation: 19.8 raisins

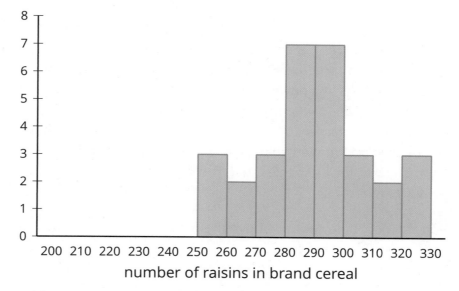

number of raisins in brand cereal

mean: 249.17 raisins, standard deviation: 26.35 raisins

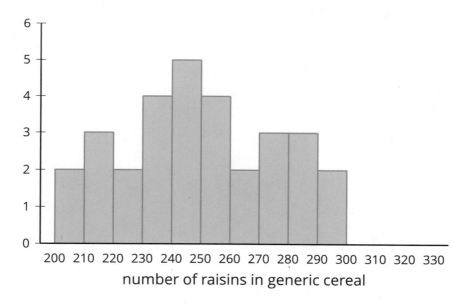

number of raisins in generic cereal

Are you ready for more?

One use of standard deviation is it gives a natural scale as to how far above or below the mean a data point is. This is incredibly useful for comparing points from two different distributions.

For example, they say you cannot compare apples and oranges, but here is a way. The average weight of a granny smith weighs 128 grams with a standard deviation of about 10 grams. The average weight of a navel orange is 140 grams with a standard deviation of about 14 grams. If we have a 148 gram granny smith apple and a 161 gram navel orange, we might wonder which is larger for its species even though they are both about 20 grams above their respective mean. We could say that the apple, which is 2 standard deviations above its mean, is larger for its species than the orange, which is only 1.5 standard deviations above its mean.

1. How many standard deviations above the mean height of a tree in forest A is its tallest tree?

2. How many standard deviations above the mean height of a tree in forest B is its tallest tree?

3. Which tree is taller in its forest?

Algebra 1 iM KH

Lesson 13 Summary

The more variation a distribution has, the greater the standard deviation. A more compact distribution will have a lesser standard deviation.

The first dot plot shows the number of points that a player on a basketball team made during each of 15 games. The second dot plot shows the number of points scored by another player during the same 15 games.

The data in the first plot has a mean of approximately 3.87 points and standard deviation of about 2.33 points. The data in the second plot has a mean of approximately 7.73 points and a standard deviation of approximately 4.67 points. The second distribution has greater variability than first distribution because the data is more spread out. This is shown in the standard deviation for the second distribution being greater than the standard deviation for the first distribution.

Standard deviation is calculated using the mean, so it makes sense to use it as a measure of variability when the mean is appropriate to use for the measure of center. In cases where the median is a more appropriate measure of center, the interquartile range is still a better measure of variability than standard deviation.

Lesson 13 Practice Problems

1. Three drivers competed in the same fifteen drag races. The mean and standard deviation for the race times of each of the drivers are given.

   Driver A had a mean race time of 4.01 seconds and a standard deviation of 0.05 seconds.

   Driver B had a mean race time of 3.96 seconds and a standard deviation of 0.12 seconds.

   Driver C had a mean race time of 3.99 seconds and a standard deviation of 0.19 seconds.

   a. Which driver had the fastest typical race time?

   b. Which driver's race times were the most variable?

   c. Which driver do you predict will win the next drag race? Support your prediction using the mean and standard deviation.

2. The widths, in millimeters, of fabric produced at a ribbon factory are collected. The mean is approximately 23 millimeters and the standard deviation is approximately 0.06 millimeters.

   Interpret the mean and standard deviation in the context of the problem.

3. Select **all** the statements that are true about standard deviation.

   A. It is a measure of center.

   B. It is a measure of variability.

   C. It is the same as the MAD.

   D. It is calculated using the mean.

   E. It is calculated using the median.

4. The number of different species of plants in some gardens is recorded.

1	2	3	4	4	5	5	6
7	8						

   a. What is the mean?

   b. What is the standard deviation?

   (From Unit 1, Lesson 12.)

5. A set of data has ten numbers. The mean of the data is 12 and the standard deviation is 0. What values could make up a data set with these statistics?

   (From Unit 1, Lesson 12.)

6. Which box plot has the largest interquartile range?

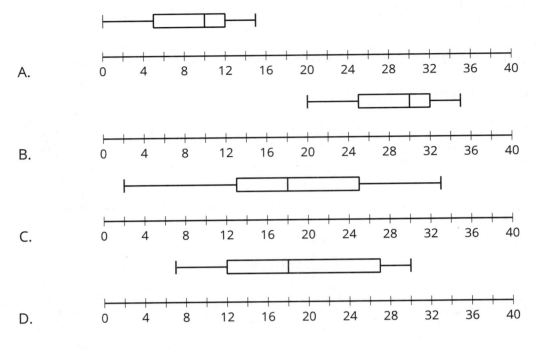

A.

B.

C.

D.

(From Unit 1, Lesson 11.)

7.   a. What is the five-number summary for 1, 3, 3, 3, 4, 8, 9, 10, 10, 17?

   b. When the maximum, 17, is removed from the data set, what is the five-number summary?

(From Unit 1, Lesson 9.)

Lesson 14: Outliers

- Let's investigate outliers and how to deal with them.

14.1: Health Care Spending

The histogram and box plot show the average amount of money, in thousands of dollars, spent on each person in the country (per capita spending) for health care in 34 countries.

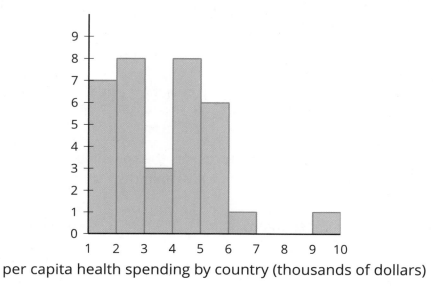

per capita health spending by country (thousands of dollars)

per capita health spending by country (thousands of dollars)

1. One value in the set is an **outlier**. Which one is it? What is its approximate value?

2. By one rule for deciding, a value is an outlier if it is more than 1.5 times the IQR greater than Q3. Show on the box plot whether or not your value meets this definition of outlier.

14.2: Investigating Outliers

Here is the data set used to create the histogram and box plot from the warm-up.

1.0803	1.0875	1.4663	1.7978	1.9702	1.9770	1.9890	2.1011
2.1495	2.2230	2.5443	2.7288	2.7344	2.8223	2.8348	3.2484
3.3912	3.5896	4.0334	4.1925	4.3763	4.5193	4.6004	4.7081
4.7528	4.8398	5.2050	5.2273	5.3854	5.4875	5.5284	5.5506
6.6475	9.8923						

1. Use technology to find the mean, standard deviation, and five-number summary.

2. The maximum value in this data set represents the spending for the United States. Should the per capita health spending for the United States be considered an outlier? Explain your reasoning.

3. Although outliers should not be removed without considering their cause, it is important to see how influential outliers can be for various statistics. Remove the value for the United States from the data set.
   a. Use technology to calculate the new mean, standard deviation, and five-number summary.

   b. How do the mean, standard deviation, median, and interquartile range of the data set with the outlier removed compare to the same summary statistics of the original data set?

14.3: Origins of Outliers

1. The number of property crime (such as theft) reports is collected for 50 colleges in California. Some summary statistics are given:

15	17	27	31	33	39	39	45
46	48	49	51	52	59	72	72
75	77	77	83	86	88	91	99
103	112	136	139	145	145	175	193
198	213	230	256	258	260	288	289
337	344	418	424	442	464	555	593
699	768						

   ○ mean: 191.1 reports

   ○ minimum: 15 reports

   ○ Q1: 52 reports

   ○ median: 107.5 reports

   ○ Q3: 260 reports

   ○ maximum: 768 reports

   a. Are any of the values outliers? Explain or show your reasoning.

   b. If there are any outliers, why do you think they might exist? Should they be included in an analysis of the data?

2. The situations described here each have an outlier. For each situation, how would you determine if it is appropriate to keep or remove the outlier when analyzing the data? Discuss your reasoning with your partner.

    a. A number cube has sides labelled 1–6. After rolling 15 times, Tyler records his data:

       1, 1, 1, 1, 2, 2, 3, 3, 4, 4, 5, 5, 5, 6, 20

    b. The dot plot represents the distribution of the number of siblings reported by a group of 20 people.

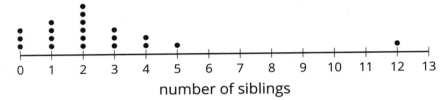

number of siblings

    c. In a science class, 12 groups of students are synthesizing biodiesel. At the end of the experiment, each group recorded the mass in grams of the biodiesel they synthesized. The masses of biodiesel are

       0, 1.245, 1.292, 1.375, 1.383, 1.412, 1.435, 1.471, 1.482, 1.501, 1.532

Are you ready for more?

Look back at some of the numerical data you and your classmates collected in the first lesson of this unit.

    1. Are any of the values outliers? Explain or show your reasoning.

    2. If there are any outliers, why do you think they might exist? Should they be included in an analysis of the data?

Lesson 14 Summary

In statistics, an **outlier** is a data value that is unusual in that it differs quite a bit from the other values in the data set.

Outliers occur in data sets for a variety of reasons including, but not limited to:

- errors in the data that result from the data collection or data entry process

- results in the data that represent unusual values that occur in the population

Outliers can reveal cases worth studying in detail or errors in the data collection process. In general, they should be included in any analysis done with the data.

A value is an outlier if it is

- more than 1.5 times the interquartile range greater than Q3 (if $x > Q3 + 1.5 \cdot IQR$)

- more than 1.5 times the interquartile range less than Q1 (if $x < Q1 - 1.5 \cdot IQR$)

In this box plot, the minimum and maximum are at least two outliers.

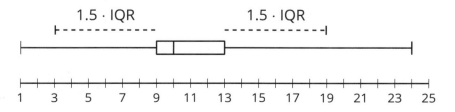

It is important to identify the source of outliers because outliers can impact measures of center and variability in significant ways. The box plot displays the resting heart rate, in beats per minute (bpm), of 50 athletes taken five minutes after a workout.

Some summary statistics include:

- mean: 69.78 bpm

- standard deviation: 10.71 bpm

- minimum: 55 bpm

- Q1: 62 bpm

- median: 70 bpm

- Q3: 76 bpm

- maximum: 112 bpm

It appears that the maximum value of 112 bpm may be an outlier. Since the interquartile range is 14 bpm ($76 - 62 = 14$) and $Q3 + 1.5 \cdot IQR = 97$, we should label the maximum value as an outlier. Searching through the actual data set, it could be confirmed that this is the only outlier.

After reviewing the data collection process, it is discovered that the athlete with the heart rate measurement of 112 bpm was taken one minute after a workout instead of five minutes after. The outlier should be deleted from the data set because it was not obtained under the right conditions.

Once the outlier is removed, the box plot and summary statistics are:

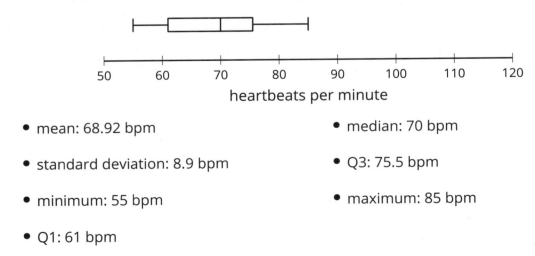

- mean: 68.92 bpm

- standard deviation: 8.9 bpm

- minimum: 55 bpm

- Q1: 61 bpm

- median: 70 bpm

- Q3: 75.5 bpm

- maximum: 85 bpm

Algebra 1 **iM KH**

The mean decreased by 0.86 bpm and the median remained the same. The standard deviation decreased by 1.81 bpm which is about 17% of its previous value. Based on the standard deviation, the data set with the outlier removed shows much less variability than the original data set containing the outlier. Since the mean and standard deviation use all of the numerical values, removing one very large data point can affect these statistics in important ways.

The median remained the same after the removal of the outlier and the IQR increased slightly. These measures of center and variability are much more resistant to change than the median and standard deviation. The median and IQR measure the middle of the data based on the number of values rather than the actual numerical values themselves, so the loss of a single value will not often have a great effect on these statistics.

The source of any possible errors should always be investigated. If the measurement of 112 beats per minute was found to be taken under the right conditions and merely included an athlete whose heart rate did not slow as much as the other athletes, it should not be deleted so that the data reflect the actual measurements. If the situation cannot be revisited to determine the source of the outlier, it should not be removed. To avoid tampering with the data and to report accurate results, data values should not be deleted unless they can be confirmed to be an error in the data collection or data entry process.

Glossary

- outlier

Lesson 14 Practice Problems

1. The number of letters received in the mail over the past week is recorded.

2	3	5	5	5	15

   Which value appears to be an outlier?

   A. 2

   B. 3

   C. 5

   D. 15

2. Elena collects 112 specimens of beetle and records their lengths for an ecology research project. When she returns to the laboratory, Elena finds that she incorrectly recorded one of lengths of the beetles as 122 centimeters (about 4 feet). What should she do with the outlier, 122 centimeters, when she analyzes her data?

3. Mai took a survey of students in her class to find out how many hours they spend reading each week. Here are some summary statistics for the data that Mai gathered:

mean: 8.5 hours   standard deviation: 5.3 hours

median: 7 hours   Q1: 5 hours   Q3: 11 hours

   a. Give an example of a number of hours larger than the median which would be an outlier. Explain your reasoning.

   b. Are there any outliers below the median? Explain your reasoning.

4. The box plot shows the statistics for the weight, in pounds, of some dogs.

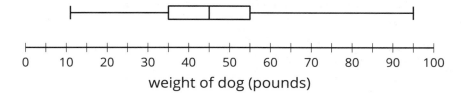

weight of dog (pounds)

Are there any outliers? Explain how you know.

5. The mean exam score for the first group of twenty examinees applying for a security job is 35.3 with a standard deviation of 3.6.

   The mean exam score for the second group of twenty examinees is 34.1 with a standard deviation of 0.5. Both distributions are close to symmetric in shape.

   a. Use the mean and standard deviation to compare the scores of the two groups.

   b. The minimum score required to get an in-person interview is 33. Which group do you think has more people get in-person interviews?

   (From Unit 1, Lesson 13.)

6. A group of pennies made in 2018 are weighed. The mean is approximately 2.5 grams with a standard deviation of 0.02 grams.

   Interpret the mean and standard deviation in terms of the context.

   (From Unit 1, Lesson 13.)

7. These values represent the expected number of paintings a person will produce over the next 10 days.

   0, 0, 0, 1, 1, 1, 2, 2, 3, 5

   a. What are the mean and standard deviation of the data?

   b. The artist is not pleased with these statistics. If the 5 is increased to a larger value, how does this impact the median, mean, and standard deviation?

   (From Unit 1, Lesson 12.)

8. List the four dot plots in order of variability from least to greatest.

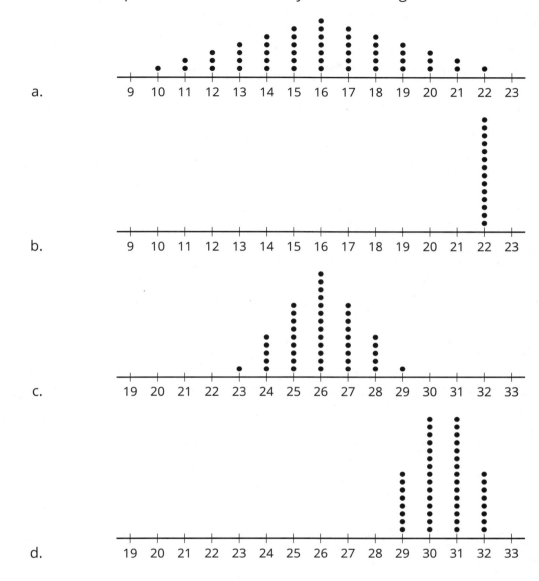

a.

b.

c.

d.

(From Unit 1, Lesson 11.)

Lesson 15: Comparing Data Sets

- Let's compare statistics for data sets.

15.1: Bowling Partners

Each histogram shows the bowling scores for the last 25 games played by each person. Choose 2 of these people to join your bowling team. Explain your reasoning.

Person A

- mean: 118.96
- median: 111
- standard deviation: 32.96
- interquartile range: 44

Person B

- mean: 131.08
- median: 129
- standard deviation: 8.64
- interquartile range: 8

Person C

- mean: 133.92
- median: 145
- standard deviation: 45.04
- interquartile range: 74

Person D

- mean: 116.56
- median: 103
- standard deviation: 56.22
- interquartile range: 31.5

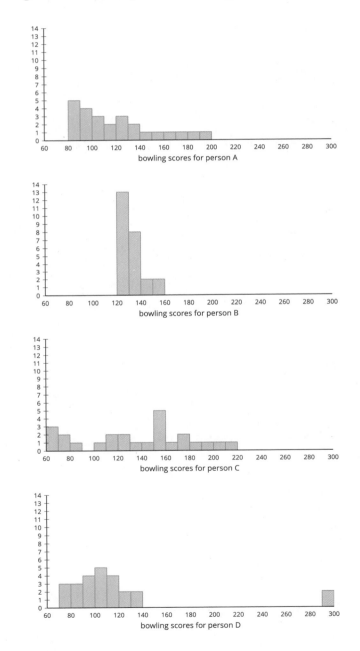

Algebra 1 iM KH

15.2: Comparing Marathon Times

All of the marathon runners from each of two different age groups have their finishing times represented in the dot plot.

ages 30 – 39 marathon finish times (minutes)

ages 40 – 49 marathon finish times (minutes)

1. Which age group tends to take longer to run the marathon? Explain your reasoning.

2. Which age group has more variable finish times? Explain your reasoning.

Are you ready for more?

1. How do you think finish times for a 20–29 age range will compare to these two distributions?

2. Find some actual marathon finish times for this group and make a box plot of your data to help compare.

15.3: Comparing Measures

For each group of data sets,

- Determine the best measure of center and measure of variability to use based on the shape of the distribution.

- Determine which set has the greatest measure of center.

- Determine which set has the greatest measure of variability.

- Be prepared to explain your reasoning.

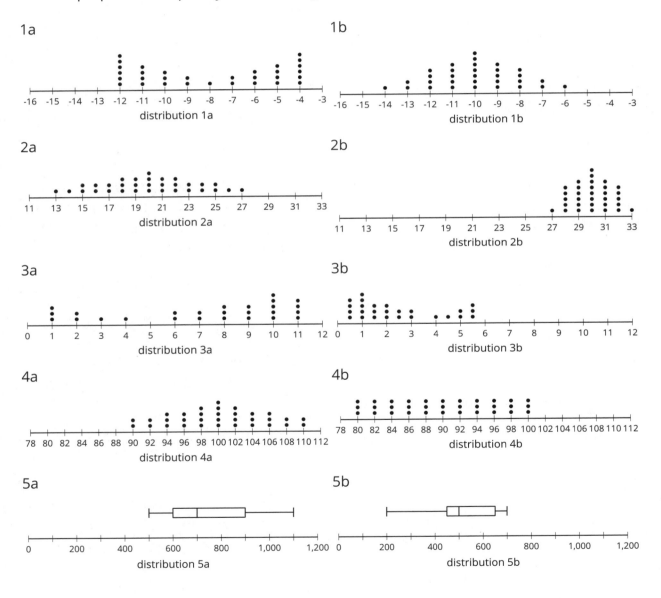

1a

distribution 1a

1b

distribution 1b

2a

distribution 2a

2b

distribution 2b

3a

distribution 3a

3b

distribution 3b

4a

distribution 4a

4b

distribution 4b

5a

distribution 5a

5b

distribution 5b

Algebra 1 iM KH

6a

A political podcast has mostly reviews that either love the podcast or hate it.

6b

A cooking podcast has reviews that neither hate nor love the podcast.

7a

Stress testing concrete from site A has all 12 samples break at 450 pounds per square inch (psi).

7b

Stress testing concrete from site B has samples break every 10 psi starting at 450 psi until the last core is broken at 560 psi.

7c

Stress testing concrete from site C has 6 samples break at 430 psi and the other 6 break at 460 psi.

Lesson 15 Summary

To compare data sets, it is helpful to look at the measures of center and measures of variability. The shape of the distribution can help choose the most useful measure of center and measure of variability.

When distributions are symmetric or approximately symmetric, the mean is the preferred measure of center and should be paired with the standard deviation as the preferred measure of variability. When distributions are skewed or when outliers are present, the median is usually a better measure of center and should be paired with the interquartile range (IQR) as the preferred measure of variability.

Once the appropriate measure of center and measure of variability are selected, these measures can be compared for data sets with similar shapes.

For example, let's compare the number of seconds it takes football players to complete a 40-yard dash at two different positions. First, we can look at a dot plot of the data to see that the tight end times do not seem symmetric, so we should probably find the median and IQR for both sets of data to compare information.

The median and IQR could be computed from the values, but can also be determined from a box plot.

wide receiver times (seconds)

tight end times (seconds)

This shows that the tight end times have a greater median (about 4.9 seconds) compared to the median of wide receiver times (about 4.5 seconds). The IQR is also greater for the tight end times (about 0.5 seconds) compared to the IQR for the wide receiver times (about 0.25 seconds).

This means that the tight ends tend to be slower in the 40-yard dash when compared to the wide receivers. The tight ends also have greater variability in their times. Together, this can be taken to mean that, in general, a typical wide receiver is faster than a typical tight end, and the wide receivers tend to have more similar times to one another than the tight ends do to one another.

Lesson 15 Practice Problems

1. Twenty students participated in a psychology experiment which measured their heart rates in two different situations.

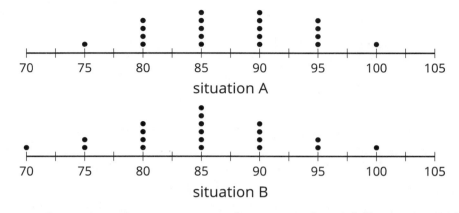

situation A

situation B

   a. What are the appropriate measures of center and variability to use with the data? Explain your reasoning.

   b. Which situation shows a greater typical heart rate?

   c. Which situation shows greater variability?

2.   a. Invent two situations that you think would result in distributions with similar measures of variability. Explain your reasoning.

   b. Invent two situations that you think would result in distributions with different measures of variability. Explain your reasoning.

3. The data set and some summary statistics are listed.

   11.5, 12.3, 13.5, 15.6, 16.7, 17.2, 18.4, 19, 19.5, 21.5

   - mean: 16.52

   - median: 16.95

   - standard deviation: 3.11

   - IQR: 5.5

   a. How does adding 5 to each of the values in the data set impact the shape of the distribution?

   b. How does adding 5 to each of the values in the data set impact the measures of center?

   c. How does adding 5 to each of the values in the data set impact the measures of variability?

4. Here are two box plots:

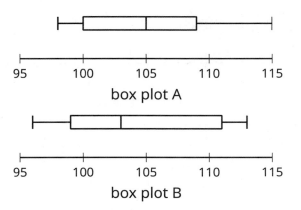

box plot A

box plot B

a. Which box plot has a greater median?

b. Which box plot has a greater measure of variability?

5. The depth of two lakes is measured at multiple spots. For the first lake, the mean depth is about 45 feet with a standard deviation of 8 feet. For the second lake, the mean depth is about 60 feet with a standard deviation of 27 feet.

Noah says the second lake is generally deeper than the first lake. Do you agree with Noah?

(From Unit 1, Lesson 13.)

6. The dot plots display the height, rounded to the nearest foot, of maple trees from two different tree farms.

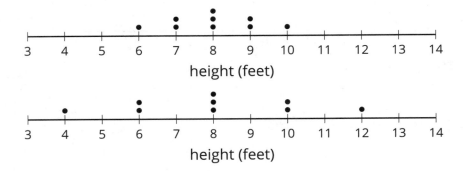

height (feet)

height (feet)

a. Compare the mean and standard deviation of the two data sets.

b. What does the standard deviation tell you about the trees at these farms?

(From Unit 1, Lesson 12.)

7. Which box plot has an IQR of 10?

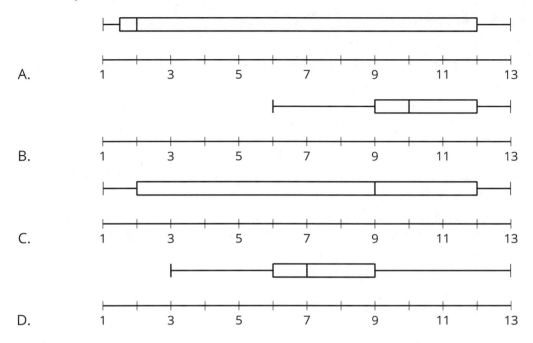

(From Unit 1, Lesson 11.)

8. What effect does eliminating the lowest value, -6, from the data set have on the mean and median?

-6, 3, 3, 3, 3, 5, 6, 6, 8, 10

(From Unit 1, Lesson 9.)

Lesson 16: Analyzing Data

- Let's answer statistical questions by analyzing data, and comparing and contrasting measures of shape, center, and variability.

16.1: Experimental Conditions

To test reaction time, the person running the test will hold a ruler at the 12 inch mark. The person whose reaction time is being tested will hold their thumb and forefinger open on either side of the flat side of the ruler at the 0 inch mark on the other side of the ruler. The person running the test will drop the ruler and the other person should close their fingers as soon as they notice the ruler moving to catch it. The distance that the ruler fell should be used as the data for this experiment.

With your partner, write a statistical question that can be answered by comparing data from two different conditions for the test.

16.2: Dropping the Ruler

Earlier, you and your partner agreed on a statistical question that can be answered using data collected in 2 different ruler-dropping conditions. With your partner, run the experiment to collect at least 20 results under each condition.

Analyze your 2 data sets to compare the statistical question. Next, create a visual display that includes:

- your statistical question

- the data you collected

- a data display

- the measure of center and variability you found that are appropriate for the data

- an answer to the statistical question with any supporting mathematical work

16.3: Heights and Handedness

Is there a connection between a student's dominant hand and their size? Use the table of information to compare the size of students with different dominant hands.

Lesson 16 Practice Problems

1. Here are the statistics for the high temperatures in a city during October:

   ○ mean of 65.3 degrees Fahrenheit

   ○ median of 63.5 degrees Fahrenheit

   ○ standard deviation of 9.3 degrees Fahrenheit

   ○ IQR of 7.1 degeres Fahrenheit

   Recall that the temperature C, measured in degrees Celsius, is related to the temperature F, measured in degrees Fahrenheit, by $C = \frac{5}{9}(F - 32)$.

   a. Describe how the value of each statistic changes when 32 is subtracted from the temperature in degrees Fahrenheit.

   b. Describe how the value of each statistic further changes when the new values are multiplied by $\frac{5}{9}$.

   c. Describe how to find the value of each statistic when the temperature is measured in degrees Celsius.

   (From Unit 1, Lesson 15.)

2. Here is a box plot.

   Give an example of a box plot that has a greater median and a greater measure of variability, but the same minimum and maximum values.

   (From Unit 1, Lesson 15.)

Algebra 1 iM KH

3. The mean vitamin C level for 20 dogs was 7.6 milligrams per liter, with a standard deviation of 2.1 milligrams per liter.

   One dog's vitamin C level was not in the normal range. It was 0.9 milligrams per liter, which is a very low level of vitamin C.

   a. If the value 0.9 is eliminated from the data set, does the mean increase or decrease?

   b. If the value 0.9 is eliminated from the data set, does the standard deviation increase or decrease?

   (From Unit 1, Lesson 14.)

4. The data set represents the number of hours that fifteen students walked during a two-week period.

6	6	7	8	8	8	9	10
10	12	13	14	15	16	30	

   The median is 10 hours, Q1 is 8, Q3 is 14, and the IQR is 6 hours. Are there any outliers in the data? Explain or show your reasoning.

   (From Unit 1, Lesson 14.)

5. Here are some summary statistics about the number of accounts that follow some bands on social media.

   ○ mean: 15,976 followers

   ○ median: 16,432 followers

   ○ standard deviation: 3,279 followers

   ○ Q1: 13,796

   ○ Q3: 19,070

   ○ IQR: 5,274 followers

   a. Give an example of a number of followers that a very popular band might have that would be considered an outlier for this data. Explain or show your reasoning.

   b. Give an example of a number of followers that a relatively unknown band might have that would be considered an outlier for this data. Explain or show your reasoning.

   (From Unit 1, Lesson 14.)

6. The weights of one population of mountain gorillas have a mean of 203 pounds and standard deviation of 18 pounds. The weights of another population of mountain gorillas have a mean of 180 pounds and standard deviation of 25 pounds. Andre says the two populations are similar. Do you agree? Explain your reasoning.

   (From Unit 1, Lesson 13.)

Algebra 1 iM KH

7. The box plot represents the distribution of the amount of change, in cents, that 50 people were carrying when surveyed.

amount of change (cents)

The box plot represents the distribution of the same data set, but with the maximum, 203, removed.

amount of change (cents)

The median is 25 cents for both plots. After examining the data, the value 203 is removed since it was an error in recording.

   a. Explain why the median remains the same when 203 cents was removed from the data set.

   b. When 203 cents is removed from the data set, does the mean remain the same? Explain your reasoning.

(From Unit 1, Lesson 10.)

Learning Targets

Lesson 1: Getting to Know You

- I can tell statistical questions from non-statistical questions and can explain the difference.

- I can tell the difference between numerical and categorical data.

Lesson 2: Data Representations

- I can find the five-number summary for data.

- I can use a dot plot, histogram, or box plot to represent data.

Lesson 3: A Gallery of Data

- I can graphically represent the data I collected and critique the representations of others.

Lesson 4: The Shape of Distributions

- I can describe the shape of a distribution using the terms "symmetric, skewed, uniform, bimodal, and bell-shaped."

- I can use a graphical representation of data to suggest a situation that produced the data pictured.

Lesson 5: Calculating Measures of Center and Variability

- I can calculate mean absolute deviation, interquartile range, mean, and median for a set of data.

Lesson 6: Mystery Computations

- I can determine basic relationships between cell values in a spreadsheet by changing the values and noticing what happens in another cell.

Lesson 7: Spreadsheet Computations

- I can use a spreadsheet as a calculator to find solutions to word problems.

Lesson 8: Spreadsheet Shortcuts

- I can use shortcuts to fill in cells on a spreadsheet.

Lesson 9: Technological Graphing

- I can create graphic representations of data and calculate statistics using technology.

Lesson 10: The Effect of Extremes

- I can describe how an extreme value will affect the mean and median.

- I can use the shape of a distribution to compare the mean and median.

Lesson 11: Comparing and Contrasting Data Distributions

- I can arrange data sets in order of variability given graphic representations.

Lesson 12: Standard Deviation

- I can describe standard deviation as a measure of variability.

- I can use technology to compute standard deviation.

Lesson 13: More Standard Deviation

- I can use standard deviation to say something about a situation.

Lesson 14: Outliers

- I can find values that are outliers, investigate their source, and figure out what to do with them.

- I can tell how an outlier will impact mean, median, IQR, or standard deviation.

Lesson 15: Comparing Data Sets

- I can compare and contrast situations using measures of center and measures of variability.

Lesson 16: Analyzing Data

- I can collect data from an experiment and compare the results using measures of center and measures of variability.

Kendall Hunt

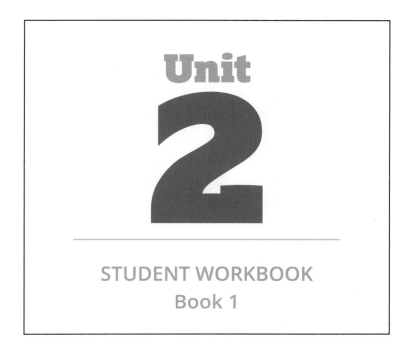

Illustrative Mathematics

ALGEBRA 1

Unit

2

STUDENT WORKBOOK

Book 1

Lesson 1: Planning a Pizza Party

- Let's write expressions to estimate the cost of a pizza party.

1.1: A Main Dish and Some Side Dishes

Here are some letters and what they represent. All costs are in dollars.

- m represents the cost of a main dish.

- n represents the number of side dishes.

- s represents the cost of a side dish.

- t represents the total cost of a meal.

1. Discuss with a partner: What does each equation mean in this situation?
    a. $m = 7.50$

    b. $m = s + 4.50$

    c. $ns = 6$

    d. $m + ns = t$

2. Write a new equation that could be true in this situation.

1.2: How Much Will It Cost?

Imagine your class is having a pizza party.

Work with your group to plan what to order and to estimate what the party would cost.

1. Record your group's plan and cost estimate. What would it take to convince the class to go with your group's plan? Be prepared to explain your reasoning.

2. Write down one or more expressions that show how your group's cost estimate was calculated.

3.   a. In your expression(s), are there quantities that might change on the day of the party? Which ones?

    b. Rewrite your expression(s), replacing the quantities that might change with letters. Be sure to specify what the letters represent.

Are you ready for more?

Find a pizza place near you and ask about the diameter and cost of at least two sizes of pizza. Compare the cost per square inch of the sizes.

1.3: What are the Constraints?

A **constraint** is something that limits what is possible or reasonable in a situation.

For example, one constraint in a pizza party might be the number of slices of pizza each person could have, s. We can write $s < 4$ to say that each person gets fewer than 4 slices.

1. Look at the expressions you wrote when planning the pizza party earlier.
   a. Choose an expression that uses one or more letters.

   b. For each letter, determine what values would be reasonable. (For instance, could the value be a non-whole number? A number greater than 50? A negative number? Exactly 2?)

2. Write equations or inequalities that represent some constraints in your pizza party plan. If a quantity must be an exact value, use the $=$ symbol. If it must be greater or less than a certain value to be reasonable, use the $<$ or $>$ symbol.

Lesson 1 Summary

Expressions, equations, and inequalities are mathematical **models**. They are mathematical representations used to describe quantities and their relationships in a real-life situation. Often, what we want to describe are constraints. A **constraint** is something that limits what is possible or what is reasonable in a situation.

For example, when planning a birthday party, we might be dealing with these quantities and constraints:

quantities

- the number of guests
- the cost of food and drinks
- the cost of birthday cake
- the cost of entertainment
- the total cost

constraints

- 20 people maximum
- $5.50 per person
- $40 for a large cake
- $15 for music and $27 for games
- no more than $180 total cost

We can use both numbers and letters to represent the quantities. For example, we can write 42 to represent the cost of entertainment, but we might use the letter n to represent the number of people at the party and the letter C for the total cost in dollars.

We can also write expressions using these numbers and letters. For instance, the expression $5.50n$ is a concise way to express the overall cost of food if it costs $5.50 per guest and there are n guests.

Sometimes a constraint is an exact value. For instance, the cost of music is $15. Other times, a constraint is a boundary or a limit. For instance, the total cost must be no more than $180. Symbols such as <, >, and = can help us express these constraints.

quantities

- the number of guests
- the cost of food and drinks
- the cost of birthday cake
- the cost of entertainment
- the total cost

constraints

- $n \leq 20$
- $5.50n$
- 40
- $15 + 27$
- $C \leq 180$

Equations can show the relationship between different quantities and constraints. For example, the total cost of the party is the sum of the costs of food, cake, entertainment. We can represent this relationship with:

$$C = 5.50n + 40 + 15 + 27 \qquad \text{or} \qquad C = 5.50n + 82$$

Deciding how to use numbers and letters to represent quantities, relationships, and constraints is an important part of mathematical modeling. Making assumptions—about the cost of food per person, for example—is also important in modeling.

A model such as $C = 5.50n + 82$ can be an efficient way to make estimates or predictions. When a quantity or a constraint changes, or when we want to know something else, we can adjust the model and perform a simple calculation, instead of repeating a series of calculations.

Glossary

- constraint
- model

Lesson 1 Practice Problems

1. The videography team entered a contest and won a monetary prize of $1,350.

   Which expression represents how much each person would get if there were x people on the team?

   A. $\frac{1350}{x}$

   B. $1350 + x$

   C. $\frac{1350}{5}$

   D. $1350 - x$

2. To support a local senior citizens center, a student club sent a flyer home to the n students in the school. The flyer said, "Please bring in money to support the senior citizens center. Paper money and coins accepted!" Their goal is to raise T dollars.

   Match each quantity to an expression, an equation, or an inequality that describes it.

   A. the dollar amount the club would have if they reached half of their goal

   B. the dollar amount the club would have if every student at the school donated 50 cents to the cause

   C. the dollar amount the club could donate if they made $50 more than their goal

   D. the dollar amount the club would still need to raise to reach its goal after every student at the school donated 50 cents

   E. the dollar amount the club would have if half of the students at the school each gave 50 cents

   1. $T + 50$

   2. $0.5T$

   3. $0.25n$

   4. $0.5n$

   5. $T - 0.5n$

3. Each of the 10 students in the baking club made 2 chocolate cakes for a fundraiser. They all used the same recipe, using C cups of flour in total.

   Write an expression that represents the amount of flour required for one cake.

4. A student club started a fundraising effort to support animal rescue organizations. The club sent an information flyer home to the n students in the school. It says, "We welcome donations of any amount, including any change you could spare!" Their goal is to raise T dollars, and to donate to a cat shelter and a dog shelter.

   Match each quantity to an expression, an equation, or an inequality that describes it.

   A. The dollar amount the club would have if they reached one-fourth of their goal.

   B. The dollar amount the club would have if every student at the school donated a quarter to the cause.

   C. The dollar amount the club could donate to the cat shelter if they reached their goal and gave a quarter of the total donation to a dog shelter.

   D. The dollar amount the club would still need to raise to reach its goal after every student at the school donated a quarter.

   E. The dollar amount the club would have if three-fourths of the students at the school each gave 50 cents.

   1. $\frac{3}{4}n \cdot \frac{1}{2}$

   2. $\frac{1}{4}T$

   3. $T - \frac{1}{4}n$

   4. $\frac{3}{4}T$

   5. $\frac{1}{4}n$

5. A softball team is ordering pizza to eat after their tournament. They plan to order cheese pizzas that cost $6 each and four-topping pizzas that cost $10 each. They order c cheese pizzas and f four-topping pizzas.

Which expression represents the total cost of all of the pizzas they order?

A. $6 + 10$

B. $c + f$

C. $6c + 10f$

D. $6f + 10c$

6. The value of coins in the pockets of several students is recorded. What is the mean of the values: 10, 20, 35, 35, 35, 40, 45, 45, 50, 60

A. 10 cents

B. 35 cents

C. 37.5 cents

D. 50 cents

(From Unit 1, Lesson 9.)

7. The dot plot displays the number of hits a baseball team made in several games. The distribution is skewed to the left.

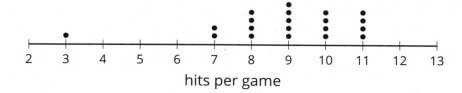

hits per game

If the game with 3 hits is considered to be recorded in error, it might be removed from the data set. If that happens:

   a. What happens to the mean of the data set?

   b. What happens to the median of the data set?

(From Unit 1, Lesson 10.)

8. A set of data has MAD 0 and one of the data values is 14. What can you say about the data values?

(From Unit 1, Lesson 11.)

Lesson 2: Writing Equations to Model Relationships (Part 1)

- Let's look at how equations can help us describe relationships and constraints.

2.1: Math Talk: Percent of 200

Evaluate mentally.

25% of 200

12% of 200

8% of 200

p% of 200

2.2: A Platonic Relationship

These three figures are called Platonic solids.

Tetrahedron   **Cube**   **Dodecahedron**

The table shows the number of vertices, edges, and faces for the tetrahedron and dodecahedron.

	faces	vertices	edges
tetrahedron	4	4	6
cube			
dodecahedron	12	20	30

1. Complete the missing values for the cube. Then, make at least two observations about the number of faces, edges, and vertices in a Platonic solid.

2. There are some interesting relationships between the number of faces (F), edges (E), and vertices (V) in all Platonic solids. For example, the number of edges is always greater than the number of faces, or $E > F$. Another example: The number of edges is always less than the sum of the number of faces and the number of vertices, or $E < F + V$.

   There is a relationship than can be expressed with an equation. Can you find it? If so, write an equation to represent it.

Are you ready for more?

There are two more Platonic solids: an octahedron which has 8 faces that are all triangles and an icosahedron which has 20 faces that are all triangles.

1. How many edges would each of these solids have? (Keep in mind that each edge is used in two faces.)

2. Use your discoveries from the activity to determine how many vertices each of these solids would have.

3. For all 5 Platonic solids, determine how many faces meet at each vertex.

2.3: Blueberries and Earnings

1. Write an equation to represent each situation.

   a. Blueberries are $4.99 a pound. Diego buys b pounds of blueberries and pays $14.95.

   b. Blueberries are $4.99 a pound. Jada buys p pounds of blueberries and pays c dollars.

   c. Blueberries are d dollars a pound. Lin buys q pounds of blueberries and pays t dollars.

   d. Noah earned n dollars over the summer. Mai earned $275, which is $45 more than Noah did.

   e. Noah earned v dollars over the summer. Mai earned m dollars, which is 45 dollars more than Noah did.

   f. Noah earned w dollars over the summer. Mai earned x dollars, which is y dollars more than Noah did.

2. How are the equations you wrote for the blueberry purchases like the equations you wrote for Mai and Noah's summer earnings? How are they different?

Algebra 1   iM KH

2.4: Car Prices

The tax on the sale of a car in Michigan is 6%. At a dealership in Ann Arbor, a car purchase also involves $120 in miscellaneous charges.

1. There are several quantities in this situation: the original car price, sales tax, miscellaneous charges, and total price. Write an equation to describe the relationship between all the quantities when:

    a. The original car price is $9,500.

    b. The original car price is $14,699.

    c. The total price is $22,480.

    d. The original price is p.

2. How would each equation you wrote change if the tax on car sales is r% and the miscellaneous charges are m dollars?

Lesson 2 Summary

Suppose your class is planning a trip to a museum. The cost of admission is $7 per person and the cost of renting a bus for the day is $180.

- If 24 students and 3 teachers are going, we know the cost will be: $7(24) + 7(3) + 180$ or $7(24 + 3) + 180$.

- If 30 students and 4 teachers are going, the cost will be: $7(30 + 4) + 180$.

Notice that the numbers of students and teachers can vary. This means the cost of admission and the total cost of the trip can also vary, because they depend on how many people are going.

Letters are helpful for representing quantities that vary. If s represents the number of students who are going, t represents the number of teachers, and C represents the total cost, we can model the quantities and constraints by writing:

$$C = 7(s + t) + 180$$

Some quantities may be fixed. In this example, the bus rental costs $180 regardless of how many students and teachers are going (assuming only one bus is needed).

Letters can also be used to represent quantities that are constant. We might do this when we don't know what the value is, or when we want to understand the relationship between quantities (rather than the specific values).

For instance, if the bus rental is B dollars, we can express the total cost of the trip as $C = 7(s + t) + B$. No matter how many teachers or students are going on the trip, B dollars need to be added to the cost of admission.

Lesson 2 Practice Problems

1. Large cheese pizzas cost $5 each and large one-topping pizzas cost $6 each.

   Write an equation that represents the total cost, T, of c large cheese pizzas and d large one-topping pizzas.

2. Jada plans to serve milk and healthy cookies for a book club meeting. She is preparing 12 ounces of milk and 4 cookies per person. Including herself, there are 15 people in the club. A package of cookies contains 24 cookies and costs $4.50.

   A 1-gallon jug of milk contains 128 ounces and costs $3. Let n represent number of people in the club, m represent the ounces of milk, c represent the number of cookies, and b represent Jada's budget in dollars.

   Select **all** of the equations that could represent the quantities and constraints in this situation.

   A. $m = 12(15)$

   B. $3m + 4.5c = b$

   C. $4n = c$

   D. $4(4.50) = c$

   E. $b = 2(3) + 3(4.50)$

3. A student on the track team runs 45 minutes each day as a part of her training. She begins her workout by running at a constant rate of 8 miles per hour for a minutes, then slows to a constant rate of 7.5 miles per hour for b minutes.

   Which equation describes the relationship between the distance she runs in miles, D, and her running speed, in miles per hour?

   A. $a + b = 45$

   B. $8a + 7.5b = D$

   C. $8(\frac{a}{60}) + 7.5(\frac{b}{60}) = D$

   D. $8(45 - b) + 7.5b = D$

Algebra 1

4. Elena bikes 20 minutes each day for exercise.

Write an equation to describe the relationship between her distance in miles, D, and her biking speed, in miles per hour, when she bikes:

    a. at a constant speed of 13 miles per hour for the entire 20 minutes

    b. at a constant speed of 15 miles per hour for the first 5 minutes, then at 12 miles per hour for the last 15 minutes

    c. at a constant speed of M miles per hour for the first 5 minutes, then at N miles per hour for the last 15 minutes

5. The dot plot displays the number of marshmallows added to hot cocoa by several kids. What is the MAD of the data represented in the dot plot?

marshmallows added to hot cocoa

    A. 0.6 marshmallows

    B. 3 marshmallows

    C. 4 marshmallows

    D. 5 marshmallows

(From Unit 1, Lesson 11.)

6. Here is a data set:

| 5 | 10 | 10 | 10 | 15 | 100 |

    a. After studying the data, the reasearcher realized that the value 100 was meant to be recorded as 15. What happens to the mean and standard deviation of the data set when the 100 is changed to a 15?

    b. For the original data set, with the 100, would the median or the mean be a better choice of measure for the center? Explain your reasoning.

(From Unit 1, Lesson 12.)

7. A coach for a little league baseball team is ordering trophies for the team. Players on the team are allowed to choose between 2 types of trophies. The gold baseball trophies cost $5.99 each and the uniform baseball trophies cost $6.49 each. The team orders g gold baseball trophies and u uniform baseball trophies.

Write an expression that could represent the total cost of all of the trophies.

(From Unit 2, Lesson 1.)

8. The robotics team needs to purchase $350 of new equipment. Each of the x students on the team plans to fundraise and contribute equally to the purchase.

Which expression represents the amount that each student needs to fundraise?

    A. $350 - x$

    B. $350 + x$

    C. $\frac{350}{x}$

    D. $350 \cdot x$

(From Unit 2, Lesson 1.)

9. In a trivia contest, players form teams and work together to earn as many points as possible for their team. Each team can have between 3 and 5 players. Each player can score up to 10 points in each round of the game. Elena and four of her friends decided to form a team and play a round.

Write an expression, an equation, or an inequality for each quantity described here. If you use a variable, specify what it represents.

   a. the number of points that Elena's team earns in one round

   b. the number of points Elena's team earns in one round if every player scores between 6 and 8 points

   c. the number of points Elena's team earns if each player misses one point

   d. the number of players in a game if there are 5 teams of 4 players each

   e. the number of players in a game if there are at least 3 teams

(From Unit 2, Lesson 1.)

Lesson 3: Writing Equations to Model Relationships (Part 2)

- Let's use patterns to help us write equations.

3.1: Finding a Relationship

Here is a table of values. The two quantities, x and y, are related.

x	y
1	0
3	8
5	24
7	48

What are some strategies you could use to find a relationship between x and y? Brainstorm as many ways as possible.

3.2: Something about 400

1. Describe in words how the two quantities in each table are related.

   ○ Table A

number of laps, x	0	1	2.5	6	9
meters run, y	0	400	1,000	2,400	3,600

   ○ Table B

meters from home, x	0	75	128	319	396
meters from school, y	400	325	272	81	4

○ Table C

electricity bills in dollars, x	85	124	309	816
total expenses in dollars, y	485	524	709	1,216

○ Table D

monthly salary in dollars, x	872	998	1,015	2,110
amount deposited in dollars, y	472	598	615	1,710

2. Match each table to an equation that represents the relationship.

- ○ Equation 1: $400 + x = y$

- ○ Equation 2: $x - 400 = y$

- ○ Equation 3: $x + y = 400$

- ○ Equation 4: $400 \cdot x = y$

Are you ready for more?

Express every number between 1 and 20 at least one way using exactly four 4's and any operation or mathematical symbol. For example, 1 could be written as $\frac{4}{4} + 4 - 4$.

3.3: What are the Relationships?

1. The table represents the relationship between the base length and the height of some parallelograms. Both measurements are in inches.

base length (inches)	height (inches)
1	48
2	24
3	16
4	12
6	8

What is the relationship between the base length and the height of these parallelograms?

2. Visitors to a carnival are invited to guess the number of beans in a jar. The person who guesses the correct number wins $300. If multiple people guess correctly, the prize will be divided evenly among them.

What is the relationship between the number of people who guess correctly and the amount of money each person will receive?

3. A $\frac{1}{2}$-gallon jug of milk can fill 8 cups, while 32 fluid ounces of milk can fill 4 cups.

What is the relationship between number of gallons and ounces? If you get stuck, try creating a table.

Lesson 3 Summary

Sometimes, the relationship between two quantities is easy to see. For instance, we know that the perimeter of a square is always 4 times the side length of the square. If P represents the perimeter and s the side length, then the relationship between the two measurements (in the same unit) can be expressed as $P = 4s$, or $s = \frac{P}{4}$.

Other times, the relationship between quantities might take a bit of work to figure out—by doing calculations several times or by looking for a pattern. Here are two examples.

- A plane departed from New Orleans and is heading to San Diego. The table shows its distance from New Orleans, x, and its distance from San Diego, y, at some points along the way.

miles from New Orleans	miles from San Diego
100	1,500
300	1,300
500	1,100
	1,020
900	700
1,450	
x	y

What is the relationship between the two distances? Do you see any patterns in how each quantity is changing? Can you find out what the missing values are?

Notice that every time the distance from New Orleans increases by some number of miles, the distance from San Diego decreases by the same number of miles, and that the sum of the two values is always 1,600 miles.

The relationship can be expressed with any of these equations:

$$x + y = 1{,}600 \qquad\qquad y = 1{,}600 - x \qquad\qquad x = 1{,}600 - y$$

- A company decides to donate $50,000 to charity. It will select up to 20 charitable organizations, as nominated by its employees. Each selected organization will receive an equal amount of donation.

  What is the relationship between the number of selected organizations, n, and the dollar amount each of them will receive, d?

  - If 5 organizations are selected, each one receives $10,000.

  - If 10 organizations are selected, each one receives $5,000.

  - If 20 organizations are selected, each one receives $2,500.

  Do you notice a pattern here? 10,000 is $\frac{50,000}{5}$, 5,000 is $\frac{50,000}{10}$, and 2,500 is $\frac{50,000}{20}$.

  We can generalize that the amount each organization receives is 50,000 divided by the number of selected organizations, or $d = \frac{50,000}{n}$.

Lesson 3 Practice Problems

1. A landscaping company is delivering crushed stone to a construction site. The table shows the total weight in pounds, W, of n loads of crushed stone.

Which equation could represent the total weight, in pounds, for n loads of crushed stone?

number of loads of crushed stone	total weight in pounds
0	0
1	2,000
2	4,000
3	6,000

A. $W = \dfrac{6{,}000}{n}$

B. $W = 6{,}000 - 2{,}000n$

C. $W = 2{,}000n$

D. $W = n + 2{,}000$

2. Members of the band sold juice and popcorn at a college football game to raise money for an upcoming trip. The band raised $2,000. The amount raised is divided equally among the m members of the band.

Which equation represents the amount, A, each member receives?

A. $A = \dfrac{m}{2{,}000}$

B. $A = \dfrac{2{,}000}{m}$

C. $A = 2{,}000m$

D. $A = 2{,}000 - m$

3. Tyler needs to complete this table for his consumer science class. He knows that 1 tablespoon contains 3 teaspoons and that 1 cup contains 16 tablespoons.

number of teaspoons	number of tablespoons	number of cups
		2
36	12	
	48	3

   a. Complete the missing values in the table.

   b. Write an equation that represents the number of teaspoons, t, contained in a cup, C.

4. The volume of dry goods, like apples or peaches, can be measured usings bushels, pecks, and quarts. A bushel contains 4 pecks, and a peck contains 8 quarts.

   What is the relationship between number of bushels, b, and the number of quarts, q? If you get stuck, try creating a table.

5. The data show the number of free throws attempted by a team in its first ten games.

2	11	11	11	12	12	13	14

14	15

The median is 12 attempts and the mean is 11.5 attempts. After reviewing the data, it is determined that 2 should not be included, since that was an exhibition game rather than a regular game during the season.

a. What happens to the median if 2 attempts is removed from the data set?

b. What happens to the mean if 2 attempts is removed from the data set?

(From Unit 1, Lesson 10.)

6. The standard deviation for a data set is 0. What can you conclude about the data?

(From Unit 1, Lesson 12.)

7. Elena has $225 in her bank account. She takes out $20 each week for w weeks. After w weeks she has d dollars left in her bank account.

   Write an equation that represents the amount of money left in her bank account after w weeks.

(From Unit 2, Lesson 2.)

8. Priya is hosting a poetry club meeting this week and plans to have fruit punch and cheese for the meeting. She is preparing 8 ounces of fruit punch per person and 2 ounces of cheese per person. Including herself, there are 12 people in the club.

   A package of cheese contains 16 ounces and costs $3.99. A one-gallon jug of fruit punch contains 128 ounces and costs $2.50. Let p represent number of people in the club, f represent the ounces of fruit punch, c represent the ounces of cheese, and b represent Priya's budget in dollars.

   Select **all** of the equations that could represent the quantities and constraints in this situation.

   A. $f = 8 \cdot 12$

   B. $c = 2 \cdot 3.99$

   C. $2 \cdot 3.99 + 2.50 = b$

   D. $2p = c$

   E. $8f + 2c = b$

(From Unit 2, Lesson 2.)

9. The density of an object can be found by taking its mass and dividing by its volume.

Write an equation to represent the relationship between the three quantities (density, mass, and volume) in each situation. Let the density, D, be measured in grams/cubic centimeters (or g/cm^3).

  a. The mass is 500 grams and the volume is 40 cubic centimeters.

  b. The mass is 125 grams and the volume is v cubic centimeters.

  c. The volume is 1.4 cubic centimeters and the density is 80 grams per cubic centimeter.

  d. The mass is m grams and the volume is v cubic centimeters.

(From Unit 2, Lesson 2.)

Lesson 4: Equations and Their Solutions

- Let's recall what we know about solutions to equations.

4.1: What is a Solution?

A granola bite contains 27 calories. Most of the calories come from c grams of carbohydrates. The rest come from other ingredients. One gram of carbohydrate contains 4 calories.

The equation $4c + 5 = 27$ represents the relationship between these quantities.

1. What could the 5 represent in this situation?

2. Priya said that neither 8 nor 3 could be the solution to the equation. Explain why she is correct.

3. Find the solution to the equation.

4.2: Weekend Earnings

Jada has time on the weekends to earn some money. A local bookstore is looking for someone to help sort books and will pay $12.20 an hour. To get to and from the bookstore on a work day, however, Jada would have to spend $7.15 on bus fare.

1. Write an equation that represents Jada's take-home earnings in dollars, E, if she works at the bookstore for h hours in one day.

2. One day, Jada takes home $90.45 after working h hours and after paying the bus fare. Write an equation to represent this situation.

3. Is 4 a solution to the last equation you wrote? What about 7?
    ○ If so, be prepared to explain how you know one or both of them are solutions.

    ○ If not, be prepared to explain why they are not solutions. Then, find the solution.

4. In this situation, what does the solution to the equation tell us?

Are you ready for more?

Jada has a second option to earn money—she could help some neighbors with errands and computer work for $11 an hour. After reconsidering her schedule, Jada realizes that she has about 9 hours available to work one day of the weekend.

Which option should she choose—sorting books at the bookstore or helping her neighbors? Explain your reasoning.

4.3: Calories from Protein and Fat

One gram of protein contains 4 calories. One gram of fat contains 9 calories. A snack has 60 calories from p grams of protein and f grams of fat.

The equation $4p + 9f = 60$ represents the relationship between these quantities.

1. Determine if each pair of values could be the number of grams of protein and fat in the snack. Be prepared to explain your reasoning.

    a. 5 grams of protein and 2 grams of fat

    b. 10.5 grams of protein and 2 grams of fat

    c. 8 grams of protein and 4 grams of fat

2. If there are 6 grams of fat in the snack, how many grams of protein are there? Show your reasoning.

3. In this situation, what does a solution to the equation $4p + 9f = 60$ tell us? Give an example of a solution.

Lesson 4 Summary

An equation that contains only one unknown quantity or one quantity that can vary is called an **equation in one variable**.

For example, the equation $2\ell + 2w = 72$ represents the relationship between the length, ℓ, and the width, w, of a rectangle that has a perimeter of 72 units. If we know that the length is 15 units, we can rewrite the equation as:

$$2(15) + 2w = 72.$$

This is an equation in one variable, because w is the only quantity that we don't know. To solve this equation means to find a value of w that makes the equation true.

In this case, 21 is the solution because substituting 21 for w in the equation results in a true statement.

$$2(15) + 2w = 72$$
$$2(15) + 2(21) = 72$$
$$30 + 42 = 72$$
$$72 = 72$$

An equation that contains two unknown quantities or two quantities that vary is called an **equation in two variables**. A solution to such an equation is *a pair* of numbers that makes the equation true.

Suppose Tyler spends $45 on T-shirts and socks. A T-shirt costs $10 and a pair of socks costs $2.50. If t represents the number of T-shirts and p represents the number of pairs of socks that Tyler buys, we can can represent this situation with the equation:

$$10t + 2.50p = 45$$

This is an equation in two variables. More than one pair of values for t and p make the equation true.

$t = 3$ and $p = 6$ $\qquad\qquad$ $t = 4$ and $p = 2$ $\qquad\qquad$ $t = 2$ and $p = 10$

$$10(3) + 2.50(6) = 45 \qquad 10(4) + 2.50(2) = 45 \qquad 10(2) + 2.50(10) = 45$$
$$30 + 15 = 45 \qquad\qquad 40 + 5 = 45 \qquad\qquad 20 + 25 = 45$$
$$45 = 45 \qquad\qquad\qquad 45 = 45 \qquad\qquad\qquad 45 = 45$$

In this situation, one constraint is that the combined cost of shirts and socks must equal $45. Solutions to the equation are pairs of t and p values that satisfy this constraint.

Combinations such as $t = 1$ and $p = 10$ or $t = 2$ and $p = 7$ are *not* solutions because they don't meet the constraint. When these pairs of values are substituted into the equation, they result in statements that are false.

Lesson 4 Practice Problems

1. An artist is selling children's crafts. Necklaces cost $2.25 each, and bracelets cost $1.50 per each.

   Select **all** the combinations of necklaces and bracelets that the artist could sell for exactly $12.00.

   A. 5 necklaces and 1 bracelet

   B. 2 necklaces and 5 bracelets

   C. 3 necklaces and 3 bracelet

   D. 4 necklaces and 2 bracelets

   E. 3 necklaces and 5 bracelets

   F. 6 necklaces and no bracelets

   G. No necklaces and 8 bracelets

2. Diego is collecting dimes and nickels in a jar. He has collected $22.25 so far. The relationship between the numbers of dimes and nickels, and the amount of money in dollars is represented by the equation $0.10d + 0.05n = 22.25$.

   Select **all** the values (d, n) that could be solutions to the equation.

   A. $(0, 445)$

   B. $(0.50, 435)$

   C. $(233, 21)$

   D. $(118, 209)$

   E. $(172, 101)$

3. Volunteer drivers are needed to bring 80 students to the championship baseball game. Drivers either have cars, which can seat 4 students, or vans, which can seat 6 students. The equation $4c + 6v = 80$ describes the relationship between the number of cars, c, and number of vans, v, that can transport exactly 80 students.

Select **all** statements that are true about the situation.

A. If 12 cars go, then 2 vans are needed.

B. $c = 14$ and $v = 4$ are a pair of solutions to the equation.

C. If 6 cars go and 11 vans go, there will be extra space.

D. 10 cars and 8 vans isn't enough to transport all the students.

E. If 20 cars go, no vans are needed.

F. 8 vans and 8 cars are numbers that meet the constraints in this situation.

4. The drama club is printing t-shirts for its members. The printing company charges a certain amount for each shirt plus a setup fee of $40. There are 21 students in the drama club.

a. If there are 21 students in the club and the t-shirt order costs a total of $187, how much does each t-shirt cost? Show your reasoning.

b. The equation $201.50 = f + 6.50(21)$ represents the cost of printing the shirts at a second printing company. Find the solution to the equation and state what it represents in this situation.

5. The box plot represents the distribution of the number of children in 30 different familes.

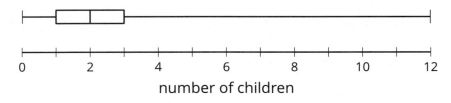

number of children

After further examination, the value of 12 is removed for having been recorded in error. The box plot represents the distribution of the same data set, but with the maximum, 12, removed.

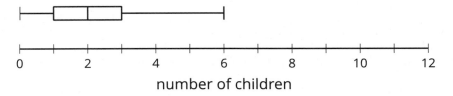

number of children

The median is 2 children for both plots.

   a. Explain why the median remains the same when 12 was removed from the data set.

   b. When 12 is removed from the data set, does mean remain the same? Explain your reasoning.

(From Unit 1, Lesson 10.)

6. The number of points Jada's basketball team scored in their games have a mean of about 44 and a standard deviation of about 15.7 points.

   Interpret the mean and standard deviation in the context of Jada's basketball team.

   (From Unit 1, Lesson 13.)

7. Kiran's family is having people over to watch a football game. They plan to serve sparkling water and pretzels. They are preparing 12 ounces of sparkling water and 3 ounces of pretzels per person. Including Kiran's family, there will be 10 people at the gathering.

   A bottle of sparkling water contains 22 ounces and costs \$1.50. A package of pretzels contains 16 ounces and costs \$2.99. Let n represent number of people watching the football game, s represent the ounces of sparkling water, p represent the ounces of pretzels, and b represent Kiran's budget in dollars. Which equation best represents Kiran's budget?

   A. $12s + 3p = b$

   B. $12 \cdot 10 + 3 \cdot 10 = b$

   C. $1.50s + 2.99p = b$

   D. $1.50 \cdot 6 + 2.99 \cdot 2 = b$

   (From Unit 2, Lesson 2.)

8. The speed of an object can be found by taking the distance it travels and dividing it by the time it takes to travel that distance. An object travels 100 feet in 2.5 seconds. Let the speed, S, be measured in feet per second.

Write an equation to represent the relationship between the three quantities (speed, distance, and time).

(From Unit 2, Lesson 2.)

9. A donut shop made 12 dozen donuts to give to a school's math club.

Which expression represents how many donuts each student would get if the donuts were equally distributed and there were x students in math club?

A. $\frac{x}{12}$

B. $\frac{12 \cdot 12}{x}$

C. $(12 \cdot 12) \cdot x$

D. $12 \cdot 12$

(From Unit 2, Lesson 1.)

Lesson 5: Equations and Their Graphs

- Let's graph equations in two variables.

5.1: Which One Doesn't Belong: Hours and Dollars

Which one doesn't belong?

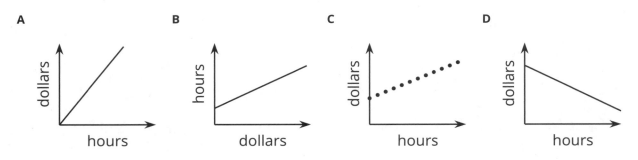

5.2: Snacks in Bulk

To get snacks for a class trip, Clare went to the "bulk" section of the grocery store, where she could buy any quantity of a product and the prices are usually good.

Clare purchased some salted almonds at $6 a pound and some dried figs at $9 per pound. She spent $75 before tax.

1. If she bought 2 pounds of almonds, how many pounds of figs did she buy?

2. If she bought 1 pound of figs, how many pounds of almonds did she buy?

3. Write an equation that describes the relationship between pounds of figs and pounds of almonds that Clare bought, and the dollar amount that she paid. Be sure to specify what the variables represent.

Algebra 1 iM **KH**

4. Here is a graph that represents the quantities in this situation.

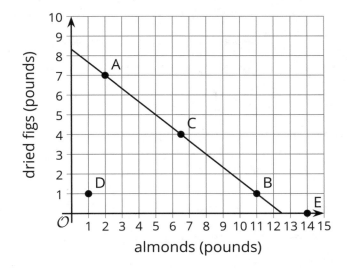

a. Choose any point on the line, state its coordinates, and explain what it tells us.

b. Choose any point that is *not* on the line, state its coordinates, and explain what it tells us.

5.3: Graph It!

1. A student has a savings account with $475 in it. She deposits $125 of her paycheck into the account every week. Her goal is to save $7,000 for college.

a. How much will be in the account after 3 weeks?

b. How long will it take before she has $1,350?

c. Write an equation that represents the relationship between the dollar amount in her account and the number of weeks of saving.

d. Graph your equation using graphing technology. Mark the points on the graph that represent the amount after 3 weeks and the week she has $1,350. Write down the coordinates.

e. How long will it take her to reach her goal?

2. A 450-gallon tank full of water is draining at a rate of 20 gallons per minute.

a. How many gallons will be in the tank after 7 minutes?

b. How long will it take for the tank to have 200 gallons?

c. Write an equation that represents the relationship between the gallons of water in the tank and minutes the tank has been draining.

d. Graph your equation using graphing technology. Mark the points on the graph that represent the gallons after 7 minutes and the time when the tank has 200 gallons. Write down the coordinates.

e. How long will it take until the tank is empty?

Are you ready for more?

1. Write an equation that represents the relationship between the gallons of water in the tank and *hours* the tank has been draining.

2. Write an equation that represents the relationship between the gallons of water in the tank and *seconds* the tank has been draining.

3. Graph each of your new equations. In what way are all of the graphs the same? In what way are they all different?

4. How would these graphs change if we used quarts of water instead of gallons? What would stay the same?

Lesson 5 Summary

Like an equation, a graph can give us information about the relationship between quantities and the constraints on them.

Suppose we are buying beans and rice to feed a large gathering of people, and we plan to spend \$120 on the two ingredients. Beans cost \$2 a pound and rice costs \$0.50 a pound.

If x represents pounds of beans and y pounds of rice, the equation $2x + 0.50y = 120$ can represent the constraints in this situation.

The graph of $2x + 0.50y = 120$ shows a straight line.

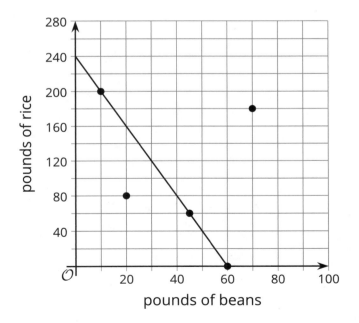

Each point on the line is a pair of x- and y-values that make the equation true and is thus a solution. It is also a pair of values that satisfy the constraints in the situation.

- The point $(10, 200)$ is on the line. If we buy 10 pounds of beans and 200 pounds of rice, the cost will be $2(10) + 0.50(200)$, which equals 120.

- The points $(60, 0)$ and $(45, 60)$ are also on the line. If we buy only beans—60 pounds of them—and no rice, we will spend \$120. If we buy 45 pounds of beans and 60 pounds of rice, we will also spend \$120.

What about points that are *not* on the line? They are not solutions because they don't satisfy the constraints, but they still have meaning in the situation.

- The point $(20, 80)$ is not on the line. Buying 20 pounds of beans and 80 pounds of rice costs $2(20) + 0.50(80)$ or 80, which does not equal 120. This combination costs less than what we intend to spend.

- The point $(70, 180)$ means that we buy 70 pounds of beans and 180 pounds of rice. It will cost $2(70) + 0.50(180)$ or 230, which is over our budget of 120.

Lesson 5 Practice Problems

1. Select **all** the points that are on the graph of the equation $4y - 6x = 12$.

    A. (-4, -3)

    B. (-1, 1.5)

    C. (0, -2)

    D. (0, 3)

    E. (3, -4)

    F. (6, 4)

2. Here is a graph of the equation $x + 3y = 6$.

    Select **all** coordinate pairs that represent a solution to the equation.

    A. (0, 2)

    B. (0, 6)

    C. (2, 6)

    D. (3, 1)

    E. (4, 1)

    F. (6, 2)

3. A theater is selling tickets to a play. Adult tickets cost $8 each and children's tickets cost $5 each. They collect $275 after selling x adult tickets and y children's tickets.

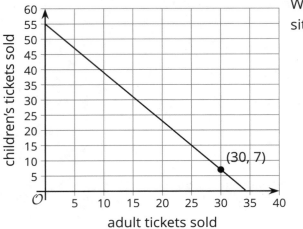

What does the point $(30, 7)$ mean in this situation?

4. *Technology required.* Priya starts with $50 in her bank account. She then deposits $20 each week for 12 weeks.

   a. Write an equation that represents the relationship between the dollar amount in her bank account and the number of weeks of saving.

   b. Graph your equation using graphing technology. Mark the point on the graph that represents the amount after 3 weeks.

   c. How many weeks does it take her to have $250 in her bank account? Mark this point on the graph.

5. During the month of August, the mean of the daily rainfall in one city was 0.04 inches with a standard deviation of 0.15 inches. In another city, the mean of the daily rainfall was 0.01 inches with a standard deviation of 0.05 inches.

Han says that both cities had a similar pattern of precipitation in the month of August. Do you agree with Han? Explain your reasoning.

(From Unit 1, Lesson 13.)

6. In a video game, players form teams and work together to earn as many points as possible for their team. Each team can have between 2 and 4 players. Each player can score up to 20 points in each round of the game. Han and three of his friends decided to form a team and play a round.

Write an expression, an equation, or an inequality for each quantity described here. If you use a variable, specify what it represents.

a. the allowable number of players on a team

b. the number of points Han's team earns in one round if every player earns a perfect score

c. the number of points Han's team earns in one round if no players earn a perfect score

d. the number of players in a game with six teams of different sizes: two teams have 4 players each and the rest have 3 players each

e. the possible number of players in a game with eight teams

(From Unit 2, Lesson 1.)

7. A student on the cross-country team runs 30 minutes a day as a part of her training.

Write an equation to describe the relationship between the distance she runs in miles, D, and her running speed, in miles per hour, when she runs:

   a. at a constant speed of 4 miles per hour for the entire 30 minutes

   b. at a constant speed of 5 miles per hour the first 20 minutes, and then at 4 miles per hour the last 10 minutes

   c. at a constant speed of 6 miles per hour the first 15 minutes, and then at 5.5 miles per hour for the remaining 15 minutes

   d. at a constant speed of a miles per hour the first 6 minutes, and then at 6.5 miles per hour for the remaining 24 minutes

   e. at a constant speed of 5.4 miles per hour for m minutes, and then at b miles per hour for n minutes

(From Unit 2, Lesson 2.)

8. In the 21st century, people measure length in feet and meters. At various points in history, people measured length in hands, cubits, and paces. There are 9 hands in 2 cubits. There are 5 cubits in 3 paces.

    a. Write an equation to express the relationship between hands, h, and cubits, c.

    b. Write an equation to express the relationship between hands, h, and paces, p.

(From Unit 2, Lesson 3.)

9. The table shows the amount of money, A, in a savings account after m months.

Select **all** the equations that represent the relationship between the amount of money, A, and the number of months, m.

number of months	dollar amount
5	1,200
6	1,300
7	1,400
8	1,500

A. $A = 100m$

B. $A = 100(m - 5)$

C. $A - 700 = 100m$

D. $A - 1{,}200 = 100m$

E. $A = 700 + 100m$

F. $A = 1200 + 100m$

G. $A = 1{,}200 + 100(m - 5)$

(From Unit 2, Lesson 3.)

Lesson 6: Equivalent Equations

- Let's investigate what makes two equations equivalent.

6.1: Two Expressions

Your teacher will assign you one of these expressions:

$$\frac{n^2 - 9}{2(4 - 3)} \qquad \text{or} \qquad (n + 3) \cdot \frac{n - 3}{8 - 3 \cdot 2}$$

Evaluate your expression when n is:

1. 5

2. 7

3. 13

4. -1

6.2: Much Ado about Ages

1. Write as many equations as possible that could represent the relationship between the ages of the two children in each family described. Be prepared to explain what each part of your equation represents.

    a. In Family A, the youngest child is 7 years younger than the oldest, who is 18.

    b. In Family B, the middle child is 5 years older than the youngest child.

2. Tyler thinks that the relationship between the ages of the children in Family B can be described with $2m - 2y = 10$, where m is the age of the middle child and y the age of the youngest. Explain why Tyler is right.

3. Are any of these equations **equivalent** to one another? If so, which ones? Explain your reasoning.

$$3a + 6 = 15 \qquad 3a = 9 \qquad a + 2 = 5 \qquad \tfrac{1}{3}a = 1$$

Are you ready for more?

Here is a puzzle:

$$m + m = N$$
$$N + N = p$$
$$m + p = Q$$
$$p + Q = \,?$$

Which expressions could be equal to $p + Q$?

$2p + m$ $\qquad\qquad$ $4m + N$ $\qquad\qquad$ $3N$ $\qquad\qquad$ $9m$

6.3: What's Acceptable?

Noah is buying a pair of jeans and using a coupon for 10% off. The total price is $56.70, which includes $2.70 in sales tax. Noah's purchase can be modeled by the equation:

$$x - 0.1x + 2.70 = 56.70$$

1. Discuss with a partner:

    a. What does the solution to the equation mean in this situation?

    b. How can you verify that 70 is not a solution but 60 is the solution?

2. Here are some equations that are related to $x - 0.1x + 2.70 = 56.70$. Each equation is a result of performing one or more moves on that original equation. Each can also be interpreted in terms of Noah's purchase.

For each equation, determine either what move was made or how the equation could be interpreted. (Some examples are given here.) Then, check if 60 is the solution of the equation.

Equation A $100x - 10x + 270 = 5,670$

    ◦ What was done?

    ◦ Interpretation?   [The price is expressed in cents instead of dollars.]

    ◦ Same solution?

Equation B $x - 0.1x = 54$

    ◦ What was done?   [Subtract 2.70 from both sides of the equation.]

    ◦ Interpretation?

    ◦ Same solution?

Equation C $0.9x + 2.70 = 56.70$

    ◦ What was done?

    ◦ Interpretation?   [10% off means paying 90% of the original price. 90% of the original price plus sales tax is $56.70.]

    ◦ Same solution?

3. Here are some other equations. For each equation, determine what move was made or how the equation could be interpreted. Then, check if 60 is the solution to the equation.

Equation D $\qquad$ $x - 0.1x = 56.70$

- What was done?

- Interpretation? [The price after using the coupon for 10% off and before sales tax is $56.70.]

- Same solution?

Equation E $\qquad$ $x - 0.1x = 59.40$

- What was done? [Subtract 2.70 from the left and add 2.70 to the right.]

- Interpretation?

- Same solution?

Equation F $\qquad$ $2(x - 0.1x + 2.70) = 56.70$

- What was done?

- Interpretation? [The price of 2 pairs of jeans, after using the coupon for 10% off and paying sales tax, is $56.70.]

- Same solution?

4. Which of the six equations are equivalent to the original equation? Be prepared to explain how you know.

Lesson 6 Summary

Suppose we bought two packs of markers and a $0.50 glue stick for $6.10. If p is the dollar cost of one pack of markers, the equation $2p + 0.50 = 6.10$ represents this purchase. The solution to this equation is 2.80.

Now suppose a friend bought six of the same packs of markers and three $0.50 glue sticks, and paid $18.30. The equation $6p + 1.50 = 18.30$ represents this purchase. The solution to this equation is also 2.80.

We can say that $2p + 0.50 = 6.10$ and $6p + 1.50 = 18.30$ are **equivalent equations** because they have exactly the same solution. Besides 2.80, no other values of p make either equation true. Only the price of $2.80 per pack of markers satisfies the constraint in each purchase.

$$2p + 0.50 = 6.10$$ How do we write equivalent equations like these?

$$6p + 1.50 = 18.30$$ There are certain moves we can perform!

In this example, the second equation, $6p + 1.50 = 18.30$, is a result of multiplying each side of the first equation by 3. Buying 3 times as many markers and glue sticks means paying 3 times as much money. The unit price of the markers hasn't changed.

Here are some other equations that are equivalent to $2p + 0.50 = 6.10$, along with the moves that led to these equations.

- $2p + 4 = 9.60$ Add 3.50 to each side of the original equation.

- $2p = 5.60$ Subtract 0.50 from each side of the original equation.

- $\frac{1}{2}(2p + 0.50) = 3.05$ Multiply each side of the original equation by $\frac{1}{2}$.

- $2(p + 0.25) = 6.10$ Apply the distributive property to rewrite the left side.

In each case:

- The move is acceptable because it doesn't change the equality of the two sides of the equation. If $2p + 0.50$ has the same value as 6.10, then multiplying $2p + 0.50$ by $\frac{1}{2}$ and multiplying 6.10 by $\frac{1}{2}$ keep the two sides equal.

- Only $p = 2.80$ makes the equation true. Any value of p that makes an equation false also makes the other equivalent equations false. (Try it!)

These moves—applying the distributive property, adding the same amount to both sides, dividing each side by the same number, and so on—might be familiar because we have performed them when solving equations. Solving an equation essentially involves writing a series of equivalent equations that eventually isolates the variable on one side.

Not all moves that we make on an equation would create equivalent equations, however!

For example, if we subtract 0.50 from the left side but add 0.50 to the right side, the result is $2p = 6.60$. The solution to this equation is 3.30, not 2.80. This means that $2p = 6.60$ is *not* equivalent to $2p + 0.50 = 6.10$.

Glossary

- equivalent equations

Lesson 6 Practice Problems

1. Which equation is equivalent to the equation $6x + 9 = 12$?

   A. $x + 9 = 6$

   B. $2x + 3 = 4$

   C. $3x + 9 = 6$

   D. $6x + 12 = 9$

2. Select **all** the equations that have the same solution as the equation $3x - 12 = 24$.

   A. $15x - 60 = 120$

   B. $3x = 12$

   C. $3x = 36$

   D. $x - 4 = 8$

   E. $12x - 12 = 24$

3. Jada has a coin jar containing n nickels and d dimes worth a total of $3.65. The equation $0.05n + 0.1d = 3.65$ is one way to represent this situation.

   Which equation is equivalent to the equation $0.05n + 0.1d = 3.65$?

   A. $5n + d = 365$

   B. $0.5n + d = 365$

   C. $5n + 10d = 365$

   D. $0.05d + 0.1n = 365$

4. Select **all** the equations that have the same solution as $2x - 5 = 15$.

   A. $2x = 10$

   B. $2x = 20$

   C. $2(x - 5) = 15$

   D. $2x - 20 = 0$

   E. $4x - 10 = 30$

   F. $15 = 5 - 2x$

5. The number of hours spent in an airplane on a single flight is recorded on a dot plot. The mean is 5 hours and the standard deviation is approximately 5.82 hours. The median is 4 hours and the IQR is 3 hours. The value 26 hours is an outlier that should not have been included in the data.

number of hours spent in an airplane

When the outlier is removed from the data set:

   a. What is the mean?

   b. What is the standard deviation?

   c. What is the median?

   d. What is the IQR?

   (From Unit 1, Lesson 14.)

6. A basketball coach purchases bananas for the players on his team. The table shows total price in dollars, P, of n bananas.

Which equation could represent the total price in dollars for n bananas?

number of bananas	total price in dollars
7	4.13
8	4.72
9	5.31
10	5.90

A. $P = 0.59n$

B. $P = 5.90 - 0.59n$

C. $P = \frac{5.90}{n}$

D. $P = n + 0.59$

(From Unit 2, Lesson 3.)

7. Kiran is collecting dimes and quarters in a jar. He has collected $10.00 so far and has d dimes and q quarters. The relationship between the numbers of dimes and quarters, and the amount of money in dollars is represented by the equation $0.1d + 0.25q = 10$.

Select **all** the values (d, q) that could be solutions to the equation.

A. $(100, 0)$

B. $(20, 50)$

C. $(50, 20)$

D. $(0, 100)$

E. $(10, 36)$

(From Unit 2, Lesson 4.)

Algebra 1 iM **KH**

8. Here is a graph of the equation $3x - 2y = 12$.

   Select **all** coordinate pairs that represent a solution to the equation.

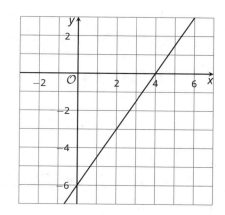

   A. $(2, -3)$

   B. $(4, 0)$

   C. $(5, -1)$

   D. $(0, -6)$

   E. $(2, 3)$

(From Unit 2, Lesson 5.)

9. Jada bought some sugar and strawberries to make strawberry jam. Sugar costs $1.80 per pound, and strawberries cost $2.50 per pound. Jada spent a total of $19.40.

   Which point on the coordinate plane could represent the pounds of sugar and strawberries that Jada used to make jam?

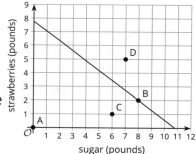

   A. Point A

   B. Point B

   C. Point C

   D. Point D

(From Unit 2, Lesson 5.)

Lesson 7: Explaining Steps for Rewriting Equations

- Let's think about why some steps for rewriting equations are valid but other steps are not.

7.1: Math Talk: Could It be Zero?

Is 0 a solution to each equation?

$4(x + 2) = 10$

$12 - 8x = 3(x + 4)$

$5x = \frac{1}{2}x$

$\frac{6}{x} + 1 = 8$

7.2: Explaining Acceptable Moves

Here are some pairs of equations. While one partner listens, the other partner should:

- Choose a pair of equations from column A. Explain why, if x is a number that makes the first equation true, then it also makes the second equation true.

- Choose a pair of equations from column B. Explain why the second equation is no longer true for a value of x that makes the first equation true.

Then, switch roles until you run out of time or you run out of pairs of equations.

	A	B
1.	$16 = 4(9 - x)$ $16 = 36 - 4x$	$9x = 5x + 4$ $14x = 4$
2.	$5x = 24 + 2x$ $3x = 24$	$\frac{1}{2}x - 8 = 9$ $x - 8 = 18$
3.	$-3(2x + 9) = 12$ $2x + 9 = -4$	$6x - 6 = 3x$ $x - 1 = 3x$
4.	$5x = 3 - x$ $5x = -x + 3$	$-11(x - 2) = 8$ $x - 2 = 8 + 11$
5.	$18 = 3x - 6 + x$ $18 = 4x - 6$	$4 - 5x = 24$ $5x = 20$

7.3: It Doesn't Work!

Noah is having trouble solving two equations. In each case, he took steps that he thought were acceptable but ended up with statements that are clearly not true.

Analyze Noah's work on each equation and the moves he made. Were they acceptable moves? Why do you think he ended up with a false equation?

Discuss your observations with your group and be prepared to share your conclusions. If you get stuck, consider solving each equation.

1.

$$x + 6 = 4x + 1 - 3x \qquad \text{original equation}$$
$$x + 6 = 4x - 3x + 1 \qquad \text{apply the commutative property}$$
$$x + 6 = x + 1 \qquad \text{combine like terms}$$
$$6 = 1 \qquad \text{subtract } x \text{ from each side}$$

2.

$$2(5 + x) - 1 = 3x + 9 \qquad \text{original equation}$$
$$10 + 2x - 1 = 3x + 9 \qquad \text{apply the distributive property}$$
$$2x - 1 = 3x - 1 \qquad \text{subtract 10 from each side}$$
$$2x = 3x \qquad \text{add 1 to each side}$$
$$2 = 3 \qquad \text{divide each side by } x$$

Are you ready for more?

1. We can't divide the number 100 by zero because dividing by zero is undefined.
    a. Instead, try dividing 100 by 10, then 1, then 0.1, then 0.01. What happens as you divide by smaller numbers?

    b. Now try dividing the number -100 by 10, by 1, by 0.1, 0.01. What is the same and what is different?

2. In middle school, you used tape diagrams to represent division. This tape diagram shows that $6 \div 2 = 3$

2	2	2

a. Draw a tape diagram that shows why $6 \div \frac{1}{2} = 12$.

b. Try to draw a tape diagram that represents $6 \div 0$. Explain why this is so difficult.

Lesson 7 Summary

When solving an equation, sometimes we end up with a false equation instead of a solution. Let's look at two examples.

Example 1: $4(x + 1) = 4x$

Here are two attempts to solve it.

$4(x + 1) = 4x$	original equation	$4(x + 1) = 4x$	original equation
$x + 1 = x$	divide each side by 4	$4x + 4 = 4x$	apply the distributive prop
$1 = 0$	subtract x from each side	$4 = 0$	subtract $4x$ from each side

Each attempt shows acceptable moves, but the final equation is a false statement. Why is that?

When solving an equation, we usually start by assuming that there is at least one value that makes the equation true. The equation $4(x + 1) = 4x$ can be interpreted as: 4 groups of $(x + 1)$ are equal to 4 groups of x. There are no values of x that can make this true.

For instance, if $x = 10$, then $x + 1 = 11$. It's not possible that 4 times 11 is equal to 4 times 10. Likewise, 1.5 is 1 more than 0.5, but 4 groups of 1.5 cannot be equal to 4 groups of 0.5.

Because of this, the moves made to solve the equation would not lead to a solution. The equation $4(x + 1) = 4$ has no solutions.

Example 2:
$$2x - 5 = \frac{x - 20}{4}$$

$2x - 5 = \dfrac{x - 20}{4}$	original equation
$8x - 20 = x - 20$	multiply each side by 4
$8x = x$	add 20 to each side
$8 = 1$	divide each side by x

Each step in the process seems acceptable, but the last equation is a false statement.

It is not easy to tell from the original equation whether it has a solution, but if we look at the equivalent equation $8x = x$, we can see that 0 could be a solution. When x is 0, the equation is $0 = 0$, which is a true statement. What is going on here?

The last move in the solving process was division by x. Because 0 could be the value of x and dividing by 0 gives an undefined number, we don't usually divide by the variable we're solving for. Doing this might make us miss a solution, namely $x = 0$.

Here are two ways to solve the equation once we get to $8x = x$:

$8x = x$		$8x = x$	
$7x = 0$	subtract x from each side	$0 = \text{-}7x$	subtract $8x$ from each side
$x = 0$	divide each side by 7	$0 = x$	divide each side by -7

Lesson 7 Practice Problems

1. Match each equation with an equivalent equation. Some of the answer choices are not used.

   A. $3x + 6 = 4x + 7$

   B. $3(x + 6) = 4x + 7$

   C. $4x + 3x = 7 - 6$

   1. $9x = 4x + 7$

   2. $3x + 18 = 4x + 7$

   3. $3x = 4x + 7$

   4. $3x - 1 = 4x$

   5. $7x = 1$

2. Mai says that equations A and B have the same solution.

   ○ Equation A: $-3(x + 7) = 24$

   ○ Equation B: $x + 7 = $ -8

   Which statement explains why this is true?

   A. Adding 3 to both sides of Equation A gives $x + 7 = $ -8.

   B. Applying the distributive property to Equation A gives $x + 7 = $ -8.

   C. Subtracting 3 from both sides of Equation A gives $x + 7 = $ -8.

   D. Dividing both sides of Equation A by -3 gives $x + 7 = $ -8.

3. Is 0 a solution to $2x + 10 = 4x + 10$? Explain or show your reasoning.

4. Kiran says that a solution to the equation $x + 4 = 20$ must also be a solution to the equation $5(x + 4) = 100$.

   Write a convincing explanation as to why this is true.

5. The entrepreneurship club is ordering potted plants for all 36 of its sponsors. One store charges $8.50 for each plant plus a delivery fee of $20. The equation $320 = x + 7.50(36)$ represents the cost of ordering potted plants at a second store.

   What does the x represent in this situation?

   A. The cost for each potted plant at the second store

   B. The delivery fee at the second store

   C. The total cost of ordering potted plants at the second store

   D. The number of sponsors of the entrepreneurship club

   (From Unit 2, Lesson 4.)

6. Which equation is equivalent to the equation $5x + 30 = 45$?

   A. $35x = 45$

   B. $5x = 75$

   C. $5(x + 30) = 45$

   D. $5(x + 6) = 45$

   (From Unit 2, Lesson 6.)

7. The environmental science club is printing T-shirts for its 15 members. The printing company charges a certain amount for each shirt plus a setup fee of $20.

If the T-shirt order costs a total of $162.50, how much does the company charge for each shirt?

(From Unit 2, Lesson 4.)

8. The graph shows the relationship between temperature in degrees Celsius and temperature in degrees Fahrenheit.

a. Mark the point on the graph that shows the temperature in Celsius when it is 60 degrees Fahrenheit.

b. Mark the point on the graph that shows the temperature in Fahrenheit when it is 60 degrees Celsius.

c. Water boils at 100 degrees Celsius. Use the graph to approximate the boiling temperature in Fahrenheit, or to confirm it, if you knew what it is.

d. The equation that converts Celsius to Fahrenheit is $C = \frac{5}{9}(F - 32)$. Use it to calculate the temperature in Celsius when it is 60 degrees Fahrenheit. (This answer will be more exact than the point you found in the first part.)

(From Unit 2, Lesson 5.)

Algebra 1 iM KH

9. Select **all** the equations that have the same solution as $2x - 5 = 15$.

   A. $2x = 10$

   B. $2x = 20$

   C. $2(x - 5) = 15$

   D. $2x - 20 = 0$

   E. $4x - 10 = 30$

   F. $15 = 5 - 2x$

(From Unit 2, Lesson 6.)

10. Diego's age d is 5 more than 2 times his sister's age s. This situation is represented by the equation $d = 2s + 5$. Which equation is equivalent to the equation $d = 2s + 5$?

   A. $d = 2(s + 5)$

   B. $d - 5 = 2s$

   C. $d - 2 = s + 5$

   D. $\frac{d}{2} = s + 5$

(From Unit 2, Lesson 6.)

Lesson 8: Which Variable to Solve for? (Part 1)

- Let's rearrange equations to pin down a certain quantity.

8.1: Which Equations?

1. The table shows the relationship between the base length, b, and the area, A, of some parallelograms. All the parallelograms have the same height. Base length is measured in inches, and area is measured in square inches. Complete the table.

b (inches)	A (square inches)
1	3
2	6
3	9
4.5	
$\frac{11}{2}$	
	36
	46.5

2. Decide whether each equation could represent the relationship between b and A. Be prepared to explain your reasoning.

   a. $b = 3A$

   b. $b = \frac{A}{3}$

   c. $A = \frac{b}{3}$

   d. $A = 3b$

8.2: Post-Parade Clean-up

After a parade, a group of volunteers is helping to pick up the trash along a 2-mile stretch of a road.

The group decides to divide the length of the road so that each volunteer is responsible for cleaning up equal-length sections.

1. Find the length of a road section for each volunteer if there are the following numbers of volunteers. Be prepared to explain or show your reasoning.

    a. 8 volunteers

    b. 10 volunteers

    c. 25 volunteers

    d. 36 volunteers

2. Write an equation that would make it easy to find ℓ, the length of a road section in miles for each volunteer, if there are n volunteers.

3. Find the number of volunteers in the group if each volunteer cleans up a section of the following lengths. Be prepared to explain or show your reasoning.

    a. 0.4 mile

    b. $\frac{2}{7}$ mile

    c. 0.125 mile

    d. $\frac{6}{45}$ mile

4. Write an equation that would make it easy to find the number of volunteers, n, if each volunteer cleans up a section that is ℓ miles.

Are you ready for more?

Let's think about the graph of the equation $y = \frac{2}{x}$.

1. Make a table of (x, y) pairs that will help you graph the equation. Make sure to include some negative numbers for x and some numbers that are not integers.

2. Plot the graph on the coordinate axes. You may need to find a few more points to plot to make the graph look smooth.

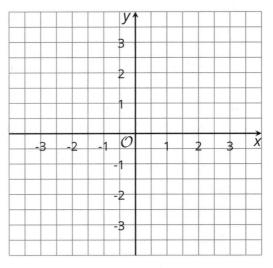

3. The coordinate plane provided is too small to show the whole graph. What do you think the graph looks like when x is between 0 and $\frac{1}{2}$? Try some values of x to test your idea.

4. What is the largest value that y can ever be?

8.3: Filling and Emptying Tanks

1. Tank A initially contained 124 liters of water. It is then filled with more water, at a constant rate of 9 liters per minute. How many liters of water are in Tank A after the following amounts of time have passed?

    a. 4 minutes

    b. 80 seconds

    c. m minutes

2. How many minutes have passed, m, when Tank A contains the following amounts of water?

   a. 151 liters

   b. 191.5 liters

   c. 270.25 liters

   d. p liters

3. Tank B, which initially contained 80 liters of water, is being drained at a rate of 2.5 liters per minute. How many liters of water remain in the tank after the following amounts of time?

   a. 30 seconds

   b. 7 minutes

   c. t minutes

4. For how many minutes, t, has the water been draining when Tank B contains the following amounts of water?

   a. 75 liters

   b. 32.5 liters

   c. 18 liters

   d. v liters

Lesson 8 Summary

A relationship between quantities can be described in more than one way. Some ways are more helpful than others, depending on what we want to find out. Let's look at the angles of an isosceles triangle, for example.

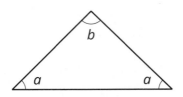

The two angles near the horizontal side have equal measurement in degrees, a.

The sum of angles in a triangle is 180°, so the relationship between the angles can be expressed as:

$$a + a + b = 180$$

Suppose we want to find a when b is 20°.

Let's substitute 20 for b and solve the equation.

$$a + a + b = 180$$
$$2a + 20 = 180$$
$$2a = 180 - 20$$
$$2a = 160$$
$$a = 80$$

What is the value of a if b is 45°?

$$a + a + b = 180$$
$$2a + 45 = 180$$
$$2a = 180 - 45$$
$$2a = 135$$
$$a = 67.5$$

Now suppose the bottom two angles are 34° each. How many degrees is the top angle?

Let's substitute 34 for a and solve the equation.

$$a + a + b = 180$$
$$34 + 34 + b = 180$$
$$68 + b = 180$$
$$b = 112$$

What is the value of b if a is 72.5°?

$$a + a + b = 180$$
$$72.5 + 72.5 + b = 180$$
$$145 + b = 180$$
$$b = 35$$

Notice that when b is given, we did the same calculation repeatedly to find a: we substituted b into the first equation, subtracted b from 180, and then divided the result by 2.

Instead of taking these steps over and over whenever we know b and want to find a, we can rearrange the equation to isolate a:

Algebra 1 iM KH

$$a + a + b = 180$$
$$2a + b = 180$$
$$2a = 180 - b$$
$$a = \frac{180 - b}{2}$$

This equation is equivalent to the first one. To find a, we can now simply substitute any value of b into this equation and evaluate the expression on right side.

Likewise, we can write an equivalent equation to make it easier to find b when we know a:

$$a + a + b = 180$$
$$2a + b = 180$$
$$b = 180 - 2a$$

Rearranging an equation to isolate one variable is called *solving for a variable*. In this example, we have solved for a and for b. All three equations are equivalent. Depending on what information we have and what we are interested in, we can choose a particular equation to use.

Lesson 8 Practice Problems

1. Priya is buying raisins and almonds to make trail mix. Almonds cost $5.20 per pound and raisins cost $2.75 per pound. Priya spent $11.70 buying almonds and raisins. The relationship between pounds of almonds a, pounds of raisins r, and the total cost is represented by the equation $5.20a + 2.75r = 11.70$.

   How many pounds of raisins did Priya buy if she bought the following amounts of almonds:

   a. 2 pounds of almonds

   b. 1.06 pounds of almonds

   c. 0.64 pounds of almonds

   d. a pounds of almonds

2. Here is a linear equation in two variables: $2x + 4y - 31 = 123$.

   Solve the equation, first for x and then for y.

3. A chef bought \$17.01 worth of ribs and chicken. Ribs cost 1.89 per pound and chicken costs 0.90 per pound. The equation $0.9c + 1.89r = 17.01$ represents the relationship between the quantities in this situation.

Show that each of the following equations is equivalent to $0.9c + 1.89r = 17.01$. Then, explain when it might be helpful to write the equation in these forms.

a. $c = 18.9 - 2.1r$

b. $r = -\frac{10}{21}c + 9$

4. A car traveled 180 miles at a constant rate.

a. Complete the table to show the rate at which the car was traveling if it completed the same distance in each number of hours.

b. Write an equation that would make it easy to find the rate at which the car was traveling in miles per hour r, if it traveled for t hours.

travel time (hours)	rate of travel (miles per hour)
5	
4.5	
3	
2.25	

5. Bananas cost $0.50 each, and apples cost $1.00 each.

   Select **all** the combinations of bananas and apples that Elena could buy for exactly $3.50.

   A. 2 bananas and 2 apples

   B. 3 bananas and 2 apples

   C. 1 banana and 2 apples

   D. 1 banana and 3 apples

   E. 5 bananas and 2 apples

   F. 5 bananas and 1 apple

   (From Unit 2, Lesson 4.)

6. A group of 280 elementary school students and 40 adults are going on a field trip. They are planning to use two different types of buses to get to the destination. The first type of bus holds 50 people and the second type of bus holds 56 people.

   Andre says that 3 of the first type of bus and 3 of the second type of bus will hold all of the students and adults going on the field trip. Is Andre correct? Explain your reasoning.

   (From Unit 2, Lesson 4.)

7. Elena says that equations A and B are not equivalent.

   ○ Equation A: $13 - 5x = 48$

   ○ Equation B: $5x = 35$

   Write a convincing explanation as to why this is true.

   (From Unit 2, Lesson 7.)

8. To grow properly, each tomato plant needs 1.5 square feet of soil and each broccoli plant needs 2.25 square feet of soil. The graph shows the different combinations of broccoli and tomato plants in an 18 square foot plot of soil.

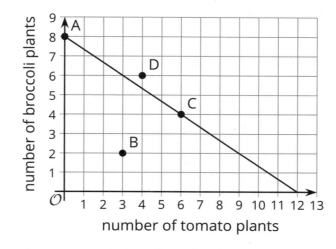

Match each point to the statement that describes it.

A. Point A

B. Point B

C. Point C

D. Point D

1. The soil is fully used when 6 tomato plants and 4 broccoli plants are planted.

2. Only broccoli was planted, but the plot is fully used and all plants can grow properly.

3. After 3 tomato plants and 2 broccoli plants were planted, there is still extra space in the plot.

4. With 4 tomato plants and 6 broccoli plants planted, the plot is overcrowded.

(From Unit 2, Lesson 5.)

9. Select **all** the equations that are equivalent to the equation $3x - 4 = 5$.

   A. $3x = 9$

   B. $3x - 4 + 4 = 5 + 4$

   C. $x - 4 = 2$

   D. $x = 9$

   E. $-4 = 5 - 3x$

(From Unit 2, Lesson 6.)

10. Han is solving an equation. He took steps that are acceptable but ended up with equations that are clearly not true.

$5x + 6 = 7x + 5 - 2x$	original equation
$5x + 6 = 7x - 2x + 5$	apply the commutative property
$5x + 6 = 5x + 5$	combine like terms
$6 = 5$	subtract $5x$ from each side

What can Han conclude as a result of these acceptable steps?

   A. There's no value of x that can make the equation $5x + 6 = 7x + 5 - 2x$ true.

   B. Any value of x can make the equation $5x + 6 = 7x + 5 - 2x$ true.

   C. $x = 6$ is a solution to the equation $5x + 6 = 7x + 5 - 2x$.

   D. $x = 5$ is a solution to the equation $5x + 6 = 7x + 5 - 2x$.

(From Unit 2, Lesson 7.)

Lesson 9: Which Variable to Solve for? (Part 2)

- Let's solve an equation for one of the variables.

9.1: Faces, Vertices, and Edges

In an earlier lesson, you saw the equation $V + F - 2 = E$, which relates the number of vertices, faces, and edges in a Platonic solid.

1. Write an equation that makes it easier to find the number of vertices in each of the Platonic solids described:

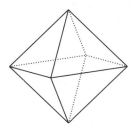

   a. An octahedron (shown here), which has 8 faces.

   b. An icosahedron, which has 30 edges.

2. A Buckminsterfullerene (also called a "Buckyball") is a polyhedron with 60 vertices. It is not a Platonic solid, but the numbers of faces, edges, and vertices are related the same way as those in a Platonic solid.

   Write an equation that makes it easier to find the number of faces a Buckyball has if we know how many edges it has.

9.2: Cargo Shipping

An automobile manufacturer is preparing a shipment of cars and trucks on a cargo ship that can carry 21,600 tons.

The cars weigh 3.6 tons each and the trucks weigh 7.5 tons each.

1. Write an equation that represents the weight constraint of a shipment. Let c be the number of cars and t be the number of trucks.

2. For one shipment, trucks are loaded first and cars are loaded afterwards. (Even though trucks are bulkier than cars, a shipment can consist of all trucks as long as it is within the weight limit.)

   Find the number of cars that can be shipped if the cargo already has:

   a. 480 trucks

   b. 1,500 trucks

   c. 2,736 trucks

   d. t trucks

3. For a different shipment, cars are loaded first, and then trucks are loaded afterwards.

   a. Write an equation you could enter into a calculator or a spreadsheet tool to find the number of trucks that can be shipped if the number of cars is known.

   b. Use your equation and a calculator or a computer to find the number of trucks that can be shipped if the cargo already has 1,000 cars. What if the cargo already has 4,250 cars?

Are you ready for more?

For yet another shipment, the manufacturer is also shipping motorcycles, which weigh 0.3 ton each.

1. Write an equation that you could enter into a calculator or a spreadsheet tool to find the number of motorcycles that can be shipped, m, if the number of cars and trucks are known.

2. Use your equation to find the number of motorcycles that can be shipped if the cargo already contains 1,200 trucks and 3,000 cars.

9.3: Streets and Staffing

The Department of Streets of a city has a budget of $1,962,800 for resurfacing roads and hiring additional workers this year.

The cost of resurfacing a mile of 2-lane road is estimated at $84,000. The average starting salary of a worker in the department is $36,000 a year.

1. Write an equation that represents the relationship between the miles of 2-lane roads the department could resurface, m, and the number of new workers it could hire, p, if it spends the entire budget.

2. Take the equation you wrote in the first question and:
   a. Solve for p. Explain what the solution represents in this situation.

   b. Solve for m. Explain what the solution represents in this situation.

3. The city is planning to hire 6 new workers and to use its entire budget.
   a. Which equation should be used to find out how many miles of 2-lane roads it could resurface? Explain your reasoning.

   b. Find the number of miles of 2-lane roads the city could resurface if it hires 6 new workers.

Lesson 9 Summary

Solving for a variable is an efficient way to find out the values that meet the constraints in a situation. Here is an example.

An elevator has a capacity of 3,000 pounds and is being loaded with boxes of two sizes—small and large. A small box weighs 60 pounds and a large box weighs 150 pounds.

Let x be the number of small boxes and y the number of large boxes. To represent the combination of small and large boxes that fill the elevator to capacity, we can write:

$$60x + 150y = 3,000$$

If there are 10 large boxes already, how many small boxes can we load onto the elevator so that it fills it to capacity? What if there are 16 large boxes?

In each case, we can substitute 10 or 16 for y and perform acceptable moves to solve the equation. Or, we can first solve for x:

$$60x + 150y = 3,000 \qquad \text{original equation}$$
$$60x = 3,000 - 150y \qquad \text{subtract } 150y \text{ from each side}$$
$$x = \frac{3,000 - 150y}{60} \qquad \text{divide each side by 60}$$

This equation allows us to easily find the number of small boxes that can be loaded, x, by substituting any number of large boxes for y.

Now suppose we first load the elevator with small boxes, say, 30 or 42, and want to know how many large boxes can be added for the elevator to reach its capacity.

We can substitute 30 or 42 for x in the original equation and solve it. Or, we can first solve for y:

$$60x + 150y = 3,000 \qquad \text{original equation}$$
$$150y = 3,000 - 60x \qquad \text{subtract } 60x \text{ from each side}$$
$$y = \frac{3,000 - 60x}{150} \qquad \text{divide each side by 150}$$

Now, for any value of x, we can quickly find y by evaluating the expression on the right side of the equal sign.

Solving for a variable—before substituting any known values—can make it easier to test different values of one variable and see how they affect the other variable. It can save us the trouble of doing the same calculation over and over.

Algebra 1 iM KH

Lesson 9 Practice Problems

1. A car has a 16-gallon fuel tank. When driven on a highway, it has a gas mileage of 30 miles per gallon. The gas mileage (also called "fuel efficiency") tells us the number of miles the car can travel for a particular amount of fuel (one gallon of gasoline, in this case). After filling the gas tank, the driver got on a highway and drove for a while.

   a. How many miles has the car traveled if it has the following amounts of gas left in the tank?

      i. 15 gallons

      ii. 10 gallons

      iii. 2.5 gallons

   b. Write an equation that represents the relationship between the distance the car has traveled in miles, d, and the amount of gas left in the tank in gallons, x.

   c. How many gallons are left in the tank when the car has traveled the following distances on the highway?

      i. 90 miles

      ii. 246 miles

   d. Write an equation that makes it easier to find the the amount of gas left in the tank, x, if we know the car has traveled d miles.

2. The area A of a rectangle is represented by the formula $A = lw$ where l is the length and w is the width. The length of the rectangle is 5.

   Write an equation that makes it easy to find the width of the rectangle if we know the area and the length.

3. Noah is helping to collect the entry fees at his school's sports game. Student entry costs $2.75 each and adult entry costs $5.25 each. At the end of the game, Diego collected $281.25.

Select **all** equations that could represent the relationship between the number of students, s, the number of adults, a, and the dollar amount received at the game.

A. $281.25 - 5.25a = 2.75s$

B. $a = 53.57 - \frac{2.75}{5.25}s$

C. $281.25 - 5.25s = a$

D. $281.25 + 2.75a = s$

E. $281.25 + 5.25s = a$

4. $V = \pi r^2 h$ is an equation to calculate the volume of a cylinder, V, where r represents the radius of the cylinder and h represents its height.

Which equation allows us to easily find the height of the cylinder because it is solved for h?

A. $r^2 h = \frac{V}{\pi}$

B. $h = V - \pi r^2$

C. $h = \frac{V}{\pi r^2}$

D. $\pi h = \frac{V}{r^2}$

5. The data represents the number of hours 10 students slept on Sunday night.

| 6 | 6 | 7 | 7 | 7 | 8 | 8 | 8 |

| 8 | 9 |

Are there any outliers? Explain your reasoning.

(From Unit 1, Lesson 14.)

6. The table shows the volume of water in cubic meters, V, in a tank after water has been pumped out for a certain number of minutes.

time after pumping begins	volume of water (cubic meters)
0	30
5	27.5
10	20
15	7.5

Which equation could represent the volume of water in cubic meters after t minutes of water being pumped out?

A. $V = 30 - 2.5t$

B. $V = 30 - 0.5t$

C. $V = 30 - 0.5t^2$

D. $V = 30 - 0.1t^2$

(From Unit 2, Lesson 4.)

7. A catering company is setting up for a wedding. They expect 150 people to attend. They can provide small tables that seat 6 people and large tables that seat 10 people.

a. Find a combination of small and large tables that seats exactly 150 people.

b. Let x represent the number of small tables and y represent the number of large tables. Write an equation to represent the relationship between x and y.

c. Explain what the point $(20, 5)$ means in this situation.

d. Is the point $(20, 5)$ a solution to the equation you wrote? Explain your reasoning.

(From Unit 2, Lesson 5.)

8. Which equation has the same solution as $10x - x + 5 = 41$?

    A. $10x + 5 = 41$

    B. $10x - 5 + x = 41$

    C. $9x = 46$

    D. $9x + 5 = 41$

    (From Unit 2, Lesson 6.)

9. Noah is solving an equation and one of his moves is unacceptable. Here are the moves he made.

$$2(x + 6) - 4 = 8 + 6x \qquad \text{original equation}$$
$$2x + 12 - 4 = 8 + 6x \qquad \text{apply the distributive property}$$
$$2x + 8 = 8 + 6x \qquad \text{combine like terms}$$
$$2x = 6x \qquad \text{subtract 8 from both sides}$$
$$2 = 6 \qquad \text{divide each side by } x$$

Which answer best explains why the "divide each side by x step" is unacceptable?

    A. When you divide both sides of $2x = 6x$ by x you get $2x^2 = 6x^2$.

    B. When you divide both sides of $2x = 6x$ by x it could lead us to think that there is no solution while in fact the solution is $x = 0$.

    C. When you divide both sides of $2x = 6x$ by x you get $2 = 6x$.

    D. When you divide both sides of $2x = 6x$ by x it could lead us to think that there is no solution while in fact the solution is $x = 3$.

    (From Unit 2, Lesson 7.)

10. Lin says that a solution to the equation $2x - 6 = 7x$ must also be a solution to the equation $5x - 6 = 10x$.

    Write a convincing explanation about why this is true.

    (From Unit 2, Lesson 7.)

Algebra 1 iM KH

Lesson 10: Connecting Equations to Graphs (Part 1)

- Let's investigate what graphs can tell us about the equations and relationships they represent.

10.1: Games and Rides

Jada has $20 to spend on games and rides at a carnival. Games cost $1 each and rides are $2 each.

1. Which equation represents the relationship between the number of games, x, and the number of rides, y, that Jada could do if she spends all her money?

   A: $x + y = 20$ B: $2x + y = 20$ C: $x + 2y = 20$

2. Explain what each of the other two equations could mean in this situation.

10.2: Graphing Games and Rides

Here are the three equations. Each represents the relationship between the number of games, x, the number of rides, y, and the dollar amount a student is spending on games and rides at a different amusement park.

Equation 1: $x + y = 20$

Equation 2: $2.50x + y = 15$

Equation 3: $x + 4y = 28$

Your teacher will assign to you (or ask you to choose) 1–2 equations. For each assigned (or chosen) equation, answer the questions.

First equation: _____

1. What's the number of rides the student could get on if they don't play any games? On the coordinate plane, mark the point that represents this situation and label the point with its coordinates.

2. What's the number of games the student could play if they don't get on any rides? On the coordinate plane, mark the point that represents this situation and label the point with its coordinates.

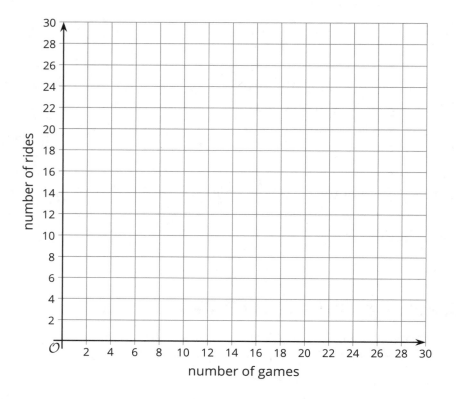

3. Draw a line to connect the two points you've drawn.

4. Complete the sentences: "If the student played no games, they can get on _____ rides. For every additional game that the student plays, x, the possible number of rides, y, _____ (increases or decreases) by _____."

5. What is the slope of your graph? Where does the graph intersect the vertical axis?

6. Rearrange the equation to solve for y.

7. What connections, if any, do you notice between your new equation and the graph?

Second equation: _____

1. What's the number of rides the student could get on if they don't play any games? On the coordinate plane, mark the point that represents this situation and label the point with its coordinates.

2. What's the number of games the student could play if they don't get on any rides? On the coordinate plane, mark the point that represents this situation and label the point with its coordinates.

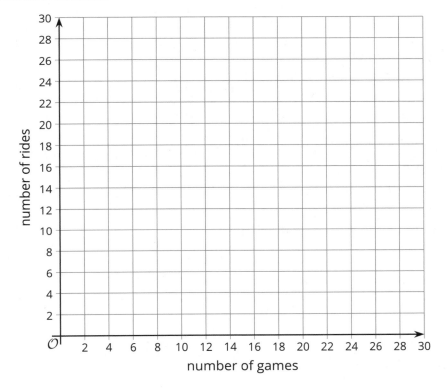

number of games

3. Draw a line to connect the two points you've drawn.

4. Complete the sentences: "If the student played no games, they can get on _____ rides. For every additional game that a student plays, x, the possible number of rides, y, _____ (increases or decreases) by _____."

5. What is the slope of your graph? Where does the graph intersect the vertical axis?

6. Rearrange the equation to solve for y.

7. What connections, if any, do you notice between your new equation and the graph?

10.3: Nickels and Dimes

Andre's coin jar contains 85 cents. There are no quarters or pennies in the jar, so the jar has all nickels, all dimes, or some of each.

1. Write an equation that relates the number of nickels, n, the number of dimes, d, and the amount of money, in cents, in the coin jar.

2. Graph your equation on the coordinate plane. Be sure to label the axes.

3. How many nickels are in the jar if there are no dimes?

4. How many dimes are in the jar if there are no nickels?

Are you ready for more?

What are all the different ways the coin jar could have 85 cents if it could also contain quarters?

Lesson 10 Summary

Linear equations can be written in different forms. Some forms allow us to better see the relationship between quantities or to predict the graph of the equation.

Suppose an athlete wishes to burn 700 calories a day by running and swimming. He burns 17.5 calories per minute of running and 12.5 calories per minute of freestyle swimming.

Let x represents the number of minutes of running and y the number of minutes of swimming. To represent the combination of running and swimming that would allow him to burn 700 calories, we can write:

$$17.5x + 12.5y = 700$$

We can reason that the more minutes he runs, the fewer minutes he has to swim to meet his goal. In other words, as x increases, y decreases. If we graph the equation, the line will slant down from left to right.

If the athlete only runs and doesn't swim, how many minutes would he need to run?

If he only swims and doesn't run, how many minutes would he need to swim?

Let's substitute 0 for y to find x:

$$17.5x + 12.5(0) = 700$$
$$17.5x = 700$$
$$x = \frac{700}{17.5}$$
$$x = 40$$

Let's substitute 0 for x to find y:

$$17.5(0) + 12.5y = 700$$
$$12.5y = 700$$
$$y = \frac{700}{12.5}$$
$$y = 56$$

On a graph, this combination of times is the point $(40, 0)$, which is the x-intercept.

On a graph, this combination of times is the point $(0, 56)$, which is the y-intercept.

If the athlete wants to know how many minutes he would need to swim if he runs for 15 minutes, 20 minutes, or 30 minutes, he can substitute each of these values for x in the equation and find y. Or, he can first solve the equation for y:

$$17.5x + 12.5y = 700$$
$$12.5y = 700 - 17.5x$$
$$y = \frac{700 - 17.5x}{12.5}$$
$$y = 56 - 1.4x$$

Notice that $y = 56 - 1.4x$, or $y = -1.4x + 56$, is written in **slope-intercept form**.

- The coefficient of x, -1.4, is the slope of the graph. It means that as x increases by 1, y falls by 1.4. For every additional minute of running, the athlete can swim 1.4 fewer minutes.

- The constant term, 56, tells us where the graph intersects the y-axis. It tells us the number minutes the athlete would need to swim if he does no running.

The first equation we wrote, $17.5x + 12.5y = 700$, is a linear equation in **standard form**. In general, it is expressed as $Ax + By = C$, where x and y are variables, and A, B, and C are numbers.

The two equations, $17.5x + 12.5y = 700$ and $y = -1.4x + 56$, are equivalent, so they have the same solutions and the same graph.

Algebra 1 iM KH

Lesson 10 Practice Problems

1. Andre bought a new bag of cat food. The next day, he opened it to feed his cat. The graph shows how many ounces were left in the bag on the days after it was bought.

a. How many ounces of food were in the bag 12 days after Andre bought it?

b. How many days did it take for the bag to contain 16 ounces of food?

c. How much did the bag weigh before it was opened?

d. About how many days did it take for the bag to be empty?

2. A little league baseball team is ordering hats.

The graph shows the relationship between the total cost, in dollars, and the number of hats ordered.

What does the slope of the graph tell us in this situation?

A. It tells us that there is a fixed cost of approximately $35 for ordering hats.

B. It tells us the amount that the total cost increases for each additional hat ordered.

C. It tell us that when 9 hats are ordered, the total cost is approximately $160.

D. It tells us that when the number of hats ordered increases by 10, the total cost increases by approximately $175.

3. A group of hikers is progressing steadily along an uphill trail. The graph shows their elevation (or height above sea level), in feet, at each distance from the start of the trail, in miles.

a. What is the slope of the graph? Show your reasoning.

b. What does the slope tell us about this situation?

c. Write an equation that represents the relationship between the hikers' distance from the start of the trail, x, and their elevation, y.

d. Does the equation $y - 250x = 500$ represent the same relationship between the distance from the start of trail and the elevation? Explain your reasoning.

4. A kindergarten teacher bought $21 worth of stickers and cardstock for his class. The stickers cost $1.50 a sheet and the cardstock cost $3.50 per pack. The equation $1.5s + 3.5c = 21$ represents the relationship between sheets of stickers, s, packs of cardstocks, c, and the dollar amount a kindergarten teacher spent on these supplies.

a. Explain how we can tell that this graph represents the given equation.

b. What do the vertical and horizontal intercepts, $(0, 6)$ and $(14, 0)$, mean in this situation?

5. In physics, the equation $PV = nRT$ is called the ideal gas law. It is used to approximate the behavior of many gases under different conditions.

P, V, and T represent pressure, volume, and temperature, n represents the number of moles of gas, and R is a constant for the ideal gas.

Which equation is solved for T?

A. $\frac{PV}{R} = nT$

B. $\frac{PV}{nR} = T$

C. $T = PV - nR$

D. $PVnR = T$

(From Unit 2, Lesson 9.)

6. To raise funds for uniforms and travel expenses, the soccer team is holding a car wash in a part of town with a lot of car and truck traffic. The team spent $90 on supplies like sponges and soap. They plan to charge $10 per car and $20 per truck. Their goal is to raise $460.

   How many cars do they have to wash if they washed the following numbers of trucks?

   a. 4 trucks

   b. 15 trucks

   c. 21 trucks

   d. 27 trucks

   e. t trucks

   (From Unit 2, Lesson 9.)

7. During the Middle Ages, people often used grains, scruples, and drahms to measure the weights of different medicines.

   If 120 grains are equivalent to 6 scruples and 6 scruples are equivalent to 2 drahms, how many drahms are equivalent to 300 grains? Explain your reasoning. If you get stuck, try creating a table.

   (From Unit 2, Lesson 3.)

8. Explain why the equation $2(3x - 5) = 6x + 8$ has no solutions.

(From Unit 2, Lesson 7.)

9. Consider the equation $3a + 0.1n = 123$. If we solve this equation for n, which equation would result?

    A. $0.1n = 123 - 3a$

    B. $n = 123 - 3a - 0.1$

    C. $n = 1{,}230 - 30a$

    D. $\dfrac{3a - 123}{0.1} = n$

(From Unit 2, Lesson 8.)

10. Diego is buying shrimp and rice to make dinner. Shrimp costs $6.20 per pound and rice costs $1.25 per pound. Diego spent $10.55 buying shrimp and rice. The relationship between pounds of shrimp s, pounds of rice r, and the total cost is represented by the equation $6.20s + 1.25r = 10.55$.

Write an equation that makes it easy to find the number of pounds of rice if we know the number of pounds of shrimp purchased.

(From Unit 2, Lesson 8.)

Lesson 11: Connecting Equations to Graphs (Part 2)

- Let's analyze different forms of linear equations and how the forms relate to their graphs.

11.1: Rewrite These!

Rewrite each quotient as a sum or a difference.

1. $\dfrac{4x - 10}{2}$

2. $\dfrac{1 - 50x}{-2}$

3. $\dfrac{5(x + 10)}{25}$

4. $\dfrac{-\frac{1}{5}x + 5}{2}$

Algebra 1 iM KH

11.2: Graphs of Two Equations

Here are two graphs that represent situations you have seen in earlier activities.

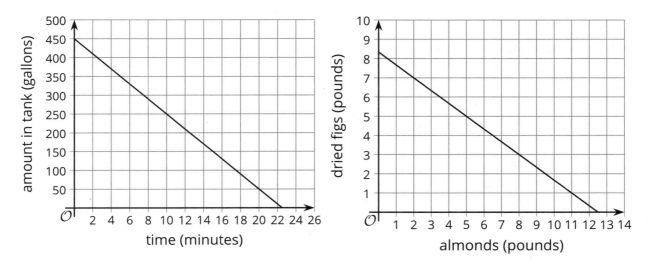

1. The first graph represents $a = 450 - 20t$, which describes the relationship between gallons of water in a tank and time in minutes.

   a. Where on the graph can we see the 450? Where can we see the -20?

   b. What do these numbers mean in this situation?

2. The second graph represents $6x + 9y = 75$. It describes the relationship between pounds of almonds and figs and the dollar amount Clare spent on them.

   Suppose a classmate says, "I am not sure the graph represents $6x + 9y = 75$ because I don't see the 6, 9, or 75 on the graph." How would you show your classmate that the graph indeed represents this equation?

11.3: Slope Match

Match each of the equations with the slope m and y-intercept of its graph.

1. $-4x + 3y = 3$

2. $12x - 4y = 8$

3. $8x + 2y = 16$

4. $-x + \frac{1}{3}y = \frac{1}{3}$

5. $-4x + 3y = -6$

A: $m = 3$, y-int $= (0, 1)$

B: $m = \frac{4}{3}$, y-int $= (0, 1)$

C: $m = \frac{4}{3}$, y-int $= (0, -2)$

D: $m = -4$, y-int $= (0, 8)$

E: $m = 3$, y-int $= (0, -2)$

Are you ready for more?

Each equation in the statement is in the form $Ax + By = C$.

1. For each equation, graph the equation and on the same coordinate plane graph the line passing through $(0, 0)$ and (A, B). What is true about each pair of lines?

2. What are the coordinates of the x-intercept and y-intercept in terms of A, B, and C?

Algebra 1   iM KH

Lesson 11 Summary

Here are two situations and two equations that represent them.

Situation 1: Mai receives a $40 bus pass. Each school day, she spends $2.50 to travel to and from school.

Let d be the number of school days since Mai receives a pass and b the balance or dollar amount remaining on the pass.

$$b = 40 - 2.50d$$

Situation 2: A student club is raising money by selling popcorn and iced tea. The club is charging $3 per bag of popcorn and $1.50 per cup of iced tea, and plans to make $60.

Let p be the bags of popcorn sold and t the cups of iced tea sold.

$$3p + 1.50t = 60$$

Here are graphs of the equations. On each graph, the coordinates of some points are shown.

The 40 in the first equation can be observed on the graph and the -2.50 can be found with a quick calculation. The graph intersects the vertical axis at 40 and the -2.50 is the slope of the line. Every time d increases by 1, b decreases by 2.50. In other words, with each passing school day, the dollar amount in Mai's bus pass drops by 2.50.

The numbers in the second equation are not as apparent on the graph. The values where the line intersects the vertical and horizontal axes, 40 and 20, are not in the equation. We can, however, reason about where they come from.

- If p is 0 (no popcorn is sold), the club would need to sell 40 cups of iced tea to make $60 because $40(1.50) = 60$.

- If t is 0 (no iced tea is sold), the club would need to sell 20 bags of popcorn to make $60 because $20(3) = 60$.

What about the slope of the second graph? We can compute it from the graph, but it is not shown in the equation $3p + 1.50t = 60$.

Notice that in the first equation, the variable b was isolated. Let's rewrite the second equation and isolate t:

$$3p + 1.50t = 60$$
$$1.50t = 60 - 3p$$
$$t = \frac{60 - 3p}{1.50}$$
$$t = 40 - 2p$$

Now the numbers in the equation can be more easily related to the graph: The 40 is where the graph intersects the vertical axis and the -2 is the slope. The slope tells us that as p increases by 1, t falls by 2. In other words, for every additional bag of popcorn sold, the club can sell 2 fewer cups of iced tea.

Lesson 11 Practice Problems

1. What is the slope of the graph of $5x - 2y = 20$?

    A. -10

    B. $\frac{-2}{5}$

    C. $\frac{5}{2}$

    D. 5

2. What is the y-intercept of each equation?

    a. $y = 6x + 2$

    b. $10x + 5y = 30$

    c. $y - 6 = 2(3x - 4)$

3. Han wanted to find the intercepts of the graph of the equation $10x + 4y = 20$. He decided to put the equation in slope-intercept form first. Here is his work:

$$10x + 4y = 20$$
$$4y = 20 - 10x$$
$$y = 5 - 10x$$

He concluded that the x-intercept is $(\frac{1}{2}, 0)$ and the y-intercept is $(0, 5)$.

    a. What error did Han make?

    b. What are the x- and y-intercepts of the line? Explain or show your reasoning.

4. Which graph represents the equation $12 = 3x + 4y$? Explain how you know.

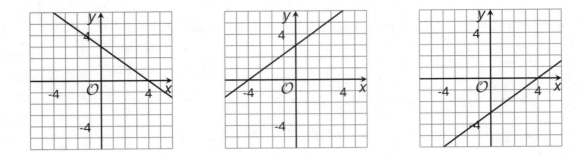

5. Clare knows that Priya has a bunch of nickels and dimes in her pocket and that the total amount is $1.25.

   a. Find one possibility for the number of nickels and number of dimes that could be in Priya's pocket.

   b. Write an equation that describes the relationship between the number of dimes and the number of nickels in Priya's pocket.

   c. Explain what the point $(13, 6)$ means in this situation.

   d. Is the point $(13, 6)$ a solution to the equation you wrote? Explain your reasoning.

   (From Unit 2, Lesson 5.)

Algebra 1 iM **KH**

6. A large company releases summary statistics about the annual salaries for its employees.

mean	standard deviation	minimum	Q1	median	Q3	maximum
$63,429	$38,439	$18,000	$50,000	$58,000	$68,000	$350,000

Based on this information, are there any outliers in the data? Explain your reasoning.

(From Unit 1, Lesson 14.)

7. The graph shows how much money Priya has in her savings account weeks after she started saving on a regular basis.

a. How much money does Priya have in the account after 10 weeks?

b. How long did it take her to save $200?

c. How much money did Priya have in her savings account when she started to save regularly?

d. Write an equation to represent the dollar amount in her savings account and the number of weeks of saving. Be sure to specify what each variable represents.

(From Unit 2, Lesson 10.)

8. Noah has a coin jar containing d dimes and q quarters worth a total of $5.00.

   Select **all** the equations that represent this situation.

   A. $d + q = 5$

   B. $d + q = 500$

   C. $0.1d + 0.25q = 5$

   D. $10d + 25q = 500$

   E. $d = 50$

   F. $q = 20$

   (From Unit 2, Lesson 6.)

9. Noah orders an extra-large pizza. It costs $12.49 for the pizza plus $1.50 for each topping. He orders an extra-large pizza with t toppings that costs a total of d dollars.

   Select **all** of the equations that represent the relationship between the number of toppings t and total cost d of the pizza with t toppings.

   A. $12.49 + t = d$

   B. $12.49 + 1.50t = d$

   C. $12.49 + 1.50d = t$

   D. $12.49 = d + 1.50t$

   E. $t = \dfrac{d - 12.49}{1.5}$

   F. $t = d - \dfrac{12.49}{1.5}$

   (From Unit 2, Lesson 9.)

Algebra 1 iM KH

10. A school sells adult tickets and student tickets for a play. It collects $1,400 in total.

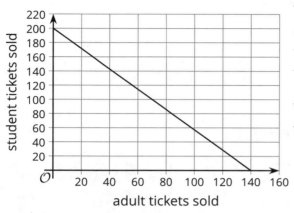

The graph shows the possible combinations of the number of adult tickets sold and the number of student tickets sold.

What does the vertical intercept (0, 200) tell us in this situation?

A. It tells us the decrease in the sale of adult tickets for each student ticket sold.

B. It tells us the decrease in the sale of student tickets for each adult ticket sold.

C. It tells us that if no adult tickets were sold, then 200 students tickets were sold.

D. It tells us that if no students tickets were sold, then 200 adult tickets were sold.

(From Unit 2, Lesson 10.)

Lesson 12: Writing and Graphing Systems of Linear Equations

- Let's recall what it means to solve a system of linear equations and how to do it by graphing.

12.1: Math Talk: A Possible Mix?

Diego bought some raisins and walnuts to make trail mix.

Raisins cost $4 a pound and walnuts cost $8 a pound. Diego spent $15 on both ingredients.

Decide if each pair of values could be a combination of raisins and walnuts that Diego bought.

4 pounds of raisins and 2 pounds of walnuts

1 pound of raisins and 1.5 pounds of walnuts

2.25 pounds of raisins and 0.75 pounds of walnuts

3.5 pounds of raisins and 1 pound of walnuts

12.2: Trail Mix

1. Here is a situation you saw earlier: Diego bought some raisins and walnuts to make trail mix. Raisins cost $4 a pound and walnuts cost $8 a pound. Diego spent $15 on both ingredients.
    a. Write an equation to represent this constraint. Let x be the pounds of raisins and y be the pounds of walnuts.

    b. Use graphing technology to graph the equation.

Algebra 1   iM **KH**

c. Complete the table with the amount of one ingredient Diego could have bought given the other. Be prepared to explain or show your reasoning.

raisins (pounds)	walnuts (pounds)
0	
0.25	
	1.375
	1.25
1.75	
3	

2. Here is a new piece of information: Diego bought a total of 2 pounds of raisins and walnuts combined.

a. Write an equation to represent this new constraint. Let x be the pounds of raisins and y be the pounds of walnuts.

b. Use graphing technology to graph the equation.

c. Complete the table with the amount of one ingredient Diego could have bought given the other. Be prepared to explain or show your reasoning.

raisins (pounds)	walnuts (pounds)
0	
0.25	
	1.375
	1.25
1.75	
3	

3. Diego spent $15 and bought exactly 2 pounds of raisins and walnuts. How many pounds of each did he buy? Explain or show how you know.

12.3: Meeting Constraints

Here are some situations that each relates two quantities and involves two constraints. For each situation, find the pair of values that meet both constraints and explain or show your reasoning.

1. A dining hall had a total of 25 tables—some long rectangular tables and some round ones. Long tables can seat 8 people. Round tables can seat 6 people. On a busy evening, all 190 seats at the tables are occupied.

   How many long tables, x, and how many round tables, y, are there?

2. A family bought a total of 16 adult and child tickets to a magic show. Adult tickets are $10.50 each and child tickets are $7.50 each. The family paid a total of $141.

   How many of adult tickets, a, and child tickets, c, did they buy?

3. At a poster shop, Han paid $16.80 for 2 large posters and 3 small posters of his favorite band. Kiran paid $14.15 for 1 large poster and 4 small posters of his favorite TV shows. Posters of the same size have the same price.

   Find the price of a large poster, ℓ, and the price of a small poster, s.

Are you ready for more?

1. Make up equations for two lines that intersect at $(4, 1)$.

2. Make up equations for three lines whose intersection points form a triangle with vertices at $(-4, 0)$, $(2, 9)$, and $(6, 5)$.

Lesson 12 Summary

A costume designer needs some silver and gold thread for the costumes for a school play. She needs a total of 240 yards. At a store that sells thread by the yard, silver thread costs $0.04 a yard and gold thread costs $0.07 a yard. The designer has $15 to spend on the thread.

How many of each color should she get if she is buying exactly what is needed and spending all of her budget?

This situation involves two quantities and two constraints—length and cost. Answering the question means finding a pair of values that meets both constraints simultaneously. To do so, we can write two equations and graph them on the same coordinate plane.

Let x represents yards of silver thread and y yards of gold thread.

- The length constraint: $x + y = 240$

- The cost constraint: $0.04x + 0.07y = 15$

Every point on the graph of $x + y = 240$ is a pair of values that meets the length constraint.

Every point on the graph of $0.04x + 0.07y = 15$ is a pair of values that meets the cost constraint.

The point where the two graphs intersect gives the pair of values that meets *both* constraints.

That point is (60, 180), which represents 60 yards of silver thread and 180 yards of gold thread.

If we substitute 60 for x and 180 for y in each equation, we find that these values make the equation true. (60, 180) is a solution to both equations simultaneously.

$$x + y = 240$$
$$60 + 180 = 240$$
$$240 = 240$$

$$0.04x + 0.07y = 15$$
$$0.04(60) + 0.07(180) = 15$$
$$2.40 + 12.60 = 15$$
$$15 = 15$$

Two or more equations that represent the constraints in the same situation form a **system of equations**. A curly bracket is often used to indicate a system.

$$\begin{cases} x + y = 240 \\ 0.04x + 0.07y = 15 \end{cases}$$

The **solution to a system of equations** is a pair of values that makes all of the equations in the system true. Graphing the equations is one way to find the solution to a system of equations.

Glossary

- solution to a system of equations
- system of equations

Algebra 1   iM **KH**

Lesson 12 Practice Problems

1. The knitting club sold 40 scarves and hats at a winter festival and made $700 from the sales. They charged $18 for each scarf and $14 for each hat.

   If s represents the number of scarves sold and h represents the number of hats sold, which system of equations represents the constraints in this situation?

   A. $\begin{cases} 40s + h = 700 \\ 18s + 14h = 700 \end{cases}$

   B. $\begin{cases} 18s + 14h = 40 \\ s + h = 700 \end{cases}$

   C. $\begin{cases} s + h = 40 \\ 18s + 14h = 700 \end{cases}$

   D. $\begin{cases} 40(s + h) = 700 \\ 18s = 14h \end{cases}$

2. Here are two equations:

   Equation 1: $6x + 4y = 34$
   Equation 2: $5x - 2y = 15$

   a. Decide whether each (x, y) pair is a solution to one equation, both equations, or neither of the equations.

      i. $(3, 4)$

      ii. $(4, 2.5)$

      iii. $(5, 5)$

      iv. $(3, 2)$

   b. Is it possible to have more than one (x, y) pair that is a solution to both equations? Explain or show your reasoning.

3. Explain or show that the point (5, -4) is a solution to this system of equations:

$$\begin{cases} 3x - 2y = 23 \\ 2x + y = 6 \end{cases}$$

4. Diego is thinking of two positive numbers. He says, "If we triple the first number and double the second number, the sum is 34."

   a. Write an equation that represents this clue. Then, find two possible pairs of numbers Diego could be thinking of.

   b. Diego then says, "If we take half of the first number and double the second, the sum is 14."

   Write an equation that could represent this description.

   c. What are Diego's two numbers? Explain or show how you know. A coordinate plane is given here, in case helpful.

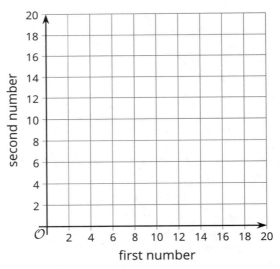

Algebra 1 iM KH

5. The table shows the volume of water in a tank after it has been filled to a certain height.

   Which equation could represent the volume of water in cubic inches, V, when the height is h inches?

height of water (inches)	volume of water (cubic inches)
0	0
1	1.05
2	8.40
3	28.35

   A. $h = V$

   B. $h = \frac{V}{4}$

   C. $V = h^2 + 0.05$

   D. $V = 1.05h^3$

(From Unit 2, Lesson 4.)

6. Andre does not understand why a solution to the equation $3 - x = 4$ must also be a solution to the equation $12 = 9 - 3x$.

   Write a convincing explanation as to why this is true.

(From Unit 2, Lesson 7.)

7. Volunteer drivers are needed to bring 80 students to the championship baseball game. Drivers either have cars, which can seat 4 students, or vans, which can seat 6 students. The equation $4c + 6v = 80$ describes the relationship between the number of cars c and number of vans v that can transport exactly 80 students.

Explain how you know that this graph represents this equation.

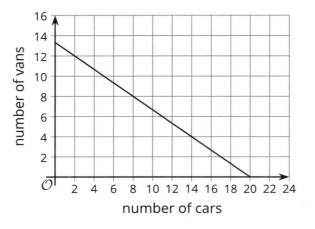

(From Unit 2, Lesson 10.)

8. Three siblings are participating in a family-friendly running event.

- The oldest sibling begins at the start line of the race and runs 7 miles per hour the entire time.

- The middle sibling begins at the start line and walks at 3.5 miles per hour throughout the race.

- The youngest sibling joins the race 4 miles from the start line and runs 5 miles per hour the rest of the way.

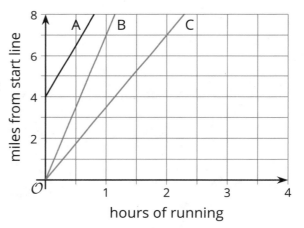

Match each graph to the sibling whose running is represented by the graph.

A. Oldest Sibling   1. Graph A

B. Middle Sibling   2. Graph B

C. Youngest Sibling   3. Graph C

(From Unit 2, Lesson 11.)

Algebra 1 iM KH

9. What is the x-intercept of the graph of $y = 3 - 5x$?

    A. $(\frac{3}{5}, 0)$

    B. $(-5, 0)$

    C. $(0, 3)$

    D. $(0, \frac{5}{3})$

(From Unit 2, Lesson 11.)

Lesson 13: Solving Systems by Substitution

- Let's use substitution to solve systems of linear equations.

13.1: Math Talk: Is It a Match?

Here are graphs of two equations in a system.

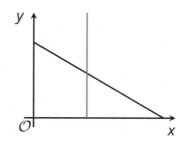

Determine if each of these systems could be represented by the graphs. Be prepared to explain how you know.

$$\begin{cases} x + 2y = 8 \\ x = \text{-}5 \end{cases} \qquad \begin{cases} y = \text{-}7x + 13 \\ y = \text{-}1 \end{cases} \qquad \begin{cases} 3x = 8 \\ 3x + y = 15 \end{cases} \qquad \begin{cases} y = 2x - 7 \\ 4 + y = 12 \end{cases}$$

13.2: Four Systems

Here are four systems of equations you saw earlier. Solve each system. Then, check your solutions by substituting them into the original equations to see if the equations are true.

A $\begin{cases} x + 2y = 8 \\ x = \text{-}5 \end{cases}$
B $\begin{cases} y = \text{-}7x + 13 \\ y = \text{-}1 \end{cases}$

C $\begin{cases} 3x = 8 \\ 3x + y = 15 \end{cases}$
D $\begin{cases} y = 2x - 7 \\ 4 + y = 12 \end{cases}$

13.3: What about Now?

Solve each system without graphing.

$$\begin{cases} 5x - 2y = 26 \\ y + 4 = x \end{cases} \qquad \begin{cases} 2m - 2p = \text{-}6 \\ p = 2m + 10 \end{cases}$$

$$\begin{cases} 2d = 8f \\ 18 - 4f = 2d \end{cases} \qquad \begin{cases} w + \frac{1}{7}z = 4 \\ z = 3w - 2 \end{cases}$$

Are you ready for more?

Solve this system with four equations. $\begin{cases} 3x + 2y - z + 5w = 20 \\ y = 2z - 3w \\ z = w + 1 \\ 2w = 8 \end{cases}$

Lesson 13 Summary

The solution to a system can usually be found by graphing, but graphing may not always be the most precise or the most efficient way to solve a system.

Here is a system of equations:

$$\begin{cases} 3p + q = 71 \\ 2p - q = 30 \end{cases}$$

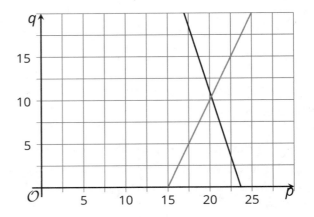

The graphs of the equations show an intersection at approximately 20 for p and approximately 10 for q.

Without technology, however, it is not easy to tell what the exact values are.

Instead of solving by graphing, we can solve the system algebraically. Here is one way.

If we subtract $3p$ from each side of the first equation, $3p + q = 71$, we get an equivalent equation: $q = 71 - 3p$. Rewriting the original equation this way allows us to isolate the variable q.

Because q is equal to $71 - 3p$, we can substitute the expression $71 - 3p$ in the place of q in the second equation. Doing this gives us an equation with only one variable, p, and makes it possible to find p.

$2p - q = 30$	original equation
$2p - (71 - 3p) = 30$	substitute $71 - 3p$ for q
$2p - 71 + 3p = 30$	apply distributive property
$5p - 71 = 30$	combine like terms
$5p = 101$	add 71 to both sides
$p = \dfrac{101}{5}$	divide both sides by 5
$p = 20.2$	

Now that we know the value of p, we can find the value of q by substituting 20.2 for p in either of the original equations and solving the equation.

Algebra 1 iM KH

$$3(20.2) + q = 71 \qquad\qquad 2(20.2) - q = 30$$
$$60.6 + q = 71 \qquad\qquad 40.4 - q = 30$$
$$q = 71 - 60.6 \qquad\qquad -q = 30 - 40.4$$
$$q = 10.4 \qquad\qquad -q = \text{-}10.4$$
$$q = \frac{\text{-}10.4}{\text{-}1}$$
$$q = 10.4$$

The solution to the system is the pair $p = 20.2$ and $q = 10.4$, or the point (20.2, 10.4) on the graph.

This method of solving a system of equations is called solving by **substitution**, because we substituted an expression for q into the second equation.

Glossary

- substitution

Lesson 13 Practice Problems

1. Identify a solution to this system of equations: $\begin{cases} -4x + 3y = 23 \\ x - y = -7 \end{cases}$

   A. $(-5, 2)$

   B. $(-2, 5)$

   C. $(-3, 4)$

   D. $(4, -3)$

2. Lin is solving this system of equations: $\begin{cases} 6x - 5y = 34 \\ 3x + 2y = 8 \end{cases}$

   She starts by rearranging the second equation to isolate the y variable: $y = 4 - 1.5x$.
   She then substituted the expression $4 - 1.5x$ for y in the first equation, as shown:

   $$6x - 5(4 - 1.5x) = 34$$
   $$6x - 20 - 7.5x = 34$$
   $$-1.5x = 54$$
   $$x = -36$$

   $$y = 4 - 1.5x$$
   $$y = 4 - 1.5 \cdot (-36)$$
   $$y = 58$$

   a. Check to see if Lin's solution of $(-36, 58)$ makes both equations in the system true.

   b. If your answer to the previous question is "no," find and explain her mistake. If your answer is "yes," graph the equations to verify the solution of the system.

3. Solve each system of equations.

a. $\begin{cases} 2x - 4y = 20 \\ x = 4 \end{cases}$

b. $\begin{cases} y = 6x + 11 \\ 2x - 3y = 7 \end{cases}$

4. Tyler and Han are trying to solve this system by substitution: $\begin{cases} x + 3y = \text{-}5 \\ 9x + 3y = 3 \end{cases}$

Tyler's first step is to isolate x in the first equation to get $x = \text{-}5 - 3y$. Han's first step is to isolate $3y$ in the first equation to get $3y = \text{-}5 - x$.

Show that both first steps can be used to solve the system and will yield the same solution.

5. The dot plots show the distribution of the length, in centimeters, of 25 shark teeth for an extinct species of shark and the length, in centimeters, of 25 shark teeth for a closely related shark species that is still living.

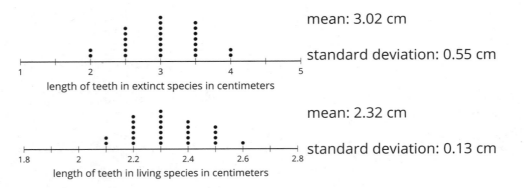

mean: 3.02 cm

standard deviation: 0.55 cm

length of teeth in extinct species in centimeters

mean: 2.32 cm

standard deviation: 0.13 cm

length of teeth in living species in centimeters

Compare the two dot plots using the shape of the distribution, measures of center, and measures of variability. Use the situation described in the problem in your explanation.

(From Unit 1, Lesson 15.)

6. Kiran buys supplies for the school's greenhouse. He buys f bags of fertilizer and p packages of soil. He pays $5 for each bag of fertilizer and $2 for each package of soil, and spends a total of $90. The equation $5f + 2p = 90$ describes this relationship.

If Kiran solves the equation for p, which equation would result?

A. $2p = 90 - 5f$

B. $p = \dfrac{5f - 90}{2}$

C. $p = 45 - 2.5f$

D. $p = \dfrac{85f}{2}$

(From Unit 2, Lesson 8.)

Algebra 1   iM KH

7. Elena wanted to find the slope and y-intercept of the graph of $25x - 20y = 100$. She decided to put the equation in slope-intercept form first. Here is her work:

$$25x - 20y = 100$$
$$20y = 100 - 25x$$
$$y = 5 - \frac{5}{4}x$$

She concluded that the slope is $-\frac{5}{4}$ and the y-intercept is $(0, 5)$.

    a. What was Elena's mistake?

    b. What are the slope and y-intercept of the line? Explain or show your reasoning.

(From Unit 2, Lesson 11.)

8. Find the x- and y-intercepts of the graph of each equation.

    a. $y = 10 - 2x$

    b. $4y + 9x = 18$

    c. $6x - 2y = 44$

    d. $2x = 4 + 12y$

(From Unit 2, Lesson 11.)

9. Andre is buying snacks for the track and field team. He buys a pounds of apricots for $6 per pound and b pounds of dried bananas for $4 per pound. He buys a total of 5 pounds of apricots and dried bananas and spends a total of $24.50.

Which system of equations represents the constraints in this situation?

A. $\begin{cases} 6a + 4b = 5 \\ a + b = 24.50 \end{cases}$

B. $\begin{cases} 6a + 4b = 24.50 \\ a + b = 5 \end{cases}$

C. $\begin{cases} 6a = 4b \\ 5(a + b) = 24.50 \end{cases}$

D. $\begin{cases} 6a + b = 4 \\ 5a + b = 24.50 \end{cases}$

(From Unit 2, Lesson 12.)

10. Here are two equations:

Equation 1: $y = 3x + 8$
Equation 2: $2x - y = \text{-}6$

Without using graphing technology:

a. Find a point that is a solution to Equation 1 but not a solution to Equation 2.

b. Find a point that is a solution to Equation 2 but not a solution to Equation 1.

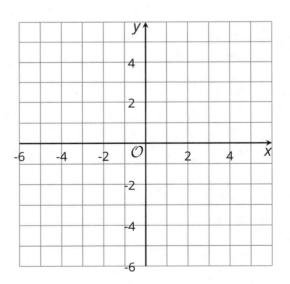

c. Graph the two equations.

d. Find a point that is a solution to both equations.

(From Unit 2, Lesson 12.)

Algebra 1 iM **KH**

Lesson 14: Solving Systems by Elimination (Part 1)

- Let's investigate how adding or subtracting equations can help us solve systems of linear equations.

14.1: Notice and Wonder: Hanger Diagrams

What do you notice? What do you wonder?

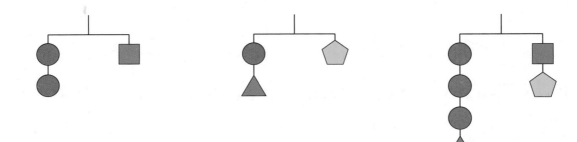

14.2: Adding Equations

Diego is solving this system of equations:

$$\begin{cases} 4x + 3y = 10 \\ \text{-}4x + 5y = 6 \end{cases}$$

Here is his work:

$$
\begin{aligned}
4x + 3y &= 10 \\
\text{-}4x + 5y &= 6 \quad + \\
\hline
0 + 8y &= 16 \\
y &= 2
\end{aligned}
$$

$$
\begin{aligned}
4x + 3(2) &= 10 \\
4x + 6 &= 10 \\
4x &= 4 \\
x &= 1
\end{aligned}
$$

1. Make sense of Diego's work and discuss with a partner:

   a. What did Diego do to solve the system?

   b. Is the pair of x and y values that Diego found actually a solution to the system? How do you know?

2. Does Diego's method work for solving these systems? Be prepared to explain or show your reasoning.

a. $\begin{cases} 2x + y = 4 \\ x - y = 11 \end{cases}$

b. $\begin{cases} 8x + 11y = 37 \\ 8x + y = 7 \end{cases}$

14.3: Adding and Subtracting Equations to Solve Systems

Here are three systems of equations you saw earlier.

System A

$\begin{cases} 4x + 3y = 10 \\ -4x + 5y = 6 \end{cases}$

System B

$\begin{cases} 2x + y = 4 \\ x - y = 11 \end{cases}$

System C

$\begin{cases} 8x + 11y = 37 \\ 8x + y = 7 \end{cases}$

For each system:

1. Use graphing technology to graph the original two equations in the system. Then, identify the coordinates of the solution.

2. Find the sum or difference of the two original equations that would enable the system to be solved.

3. Graph the third equation on the same coordinate plane. Make an observation about the graph.

Are you ready for more?

Mai wonders what would happen if we multiply equations. That is, we multiply the expressions on the left side of the two equations and set them equal to the expressions on the right side of the two equations.

1. In system B write out an equation that you would get if you multiply the two equations in this manner.

2. Does your original solution still work in this new equation?

3. Use graphing technology to graph this new equation on the same coordinate plane. Why is this approach not particularly helpful?

Lesson 14 Summary

Another way to solve systems of equations algebraically is by **elimination**. Just like in substitution, the idea is to eliminate one variable so that we can solve for the other. This is done by adding or subtracting equations in the system. Let's look at an example.

$$\begin{cases} 5x + 7y = 64 \\ 0.5x - 7y = \text{-}9 \end{cases}$$

Notice that one equation has $7y$ and the other has $\text{-}7y$.

If we add the second equation to the first, the $7y$ and $\text{-}7y$ add up to 0, which eliminates the y-variable, allowing us to solve for x.

$$\begin{aligned} 5x + 7y &= 64 \\ 0.5x - 7y &= \text{-}9 \quad + \\ \hline 5.5x + 0 &= 55 \\ 5.5x &= 55 \\ x &= 10 \end{aligned}$$

Now that we know $x = 10$, we can substitute 10 for x in either of the equations and find y:

$$\begin{aligned} 5x + 7y &= 64 \\ 5(10) + 7y &= 64 \\ 50 + 7y &= 64 \\ 7y &= 14 \\ y &= 2 \end{aligned}$$

$$\begin{aligned} 0.5x - 7y &= \text{-}9 \\ 0.5(10) - 7y &= \text{-}9 \\ 5 - 7y &= \text{-}9 \\ \text{-}7y &= \text{-}14 \\ y &= 2 \end{aligned}$$

In this system, the coefficient of y in the first equation happens to be the opposite of the coefficient of y in the second equation. The sum of the terms with y-variables is 0.

What if the equations don't have opposite coefficients for the same variable, like in the following system?

$$\begin{cases} 8r + 4s = 12 \\ 8r + s = \text{-}3 \end{cases}$$

Notice that both equations have $8r$ and if we subtract the second equation from the first, the variable r will be eliminated because $8r - 8r$ is 0.

$$\begin{aligned} 8r + 4s &= 12 \\ 8r + s &= \text{-}3 \quad - \\ \hline 0 + 3s &= 15 \\ 3s &= 15 \\ s &= 5 \end{aligned}$$

Substituting 5 for s in one of the equations gives us r:

$$\begin{aligned} 8r + 4s &= 12 \\ 8r + 4(5) &= 12 \\ 8r + 20 &= 12 \\ 8r &= \text{-}8 \\ r &= \text{-}1 \end{aligned}$$

Adding or subtracting the equations in a system creates a new equation. How do we know the new equation shares a solution with the original system?

If we graph the original equations in the system and the new equation, we can see that all three lines intersect at the same point, but why do they?

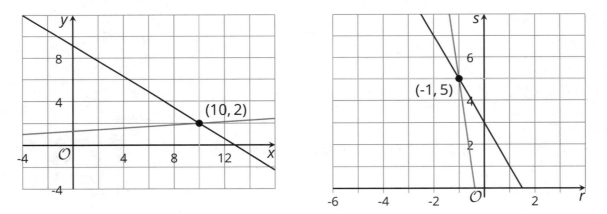

In future lessons, we will investigate why this strategy works.

Glossary

- elimination

Algebra 1 iM KH

Lesson 14 Practice Problems

1. Which equation is the result of adding these two equations?

$$\begin{cases} -2x + 4y = 17 \\ 3x - 10y = \text{-}3 \end{cases}$$

   A. $\text{-}5x - 6y = 14$

   B. $\text{-}x - 6y = 14$

   C. $x - 6y = 14$

   D. $5x + 14y = 20$

2. Which equation is the result of subtracting the second equation from the first?

$$\begin{cases} 4x - 6y = 13 \\ \text{-}5x + 2y = 5 \end{cases}$$

   A. $\text{-}9x - 4y = 8$

   B. $\text{-}x + 4y = 8$

   C. $x - 4y = 8$

   D. $9x - 8y = 8$

3. Solve this system of equations without graphing: $\begin{cases} 5x + 2y = 29 \\ 5x - 2y = 41 \end{cases}$

4. Here is a system of linear equations: $\begin{cases} 6x + 21y = 103 \\ \text{-}6x + 23y = 51 \end{cases}$

   Would you rather use subtraction or addition to solve the system? Explain your reasoning.

5. Kiran sells f full boxes and h half-boxes of fruit to raise money for a band trip. He earns \$5 for each full box and \$2 for each half-box of fruit he sells and earns a total of \$100 toward the cost of his band trip. The equation $5f + 2h = 100$ describes this relationship.

Solve the equation for f.

(From Unit 2, Lesson 8.)

6. Match each equation with the corresponding equation solved for a.

A. $a + 2b = 5$

B. $5a = 2b$

C. $a + 5 = 2b$

D. $5(a + 2b) = 0$

E. $5a + 2b = 0$

1. $a = \frac{2b}{5}$

2. $a = \frac{-2b}{5}$

3. $a = -2b$

4. $a = 2b - 5$

5. $a = 5 - 2b$

(From Unit 2, Lesson 8.)

7. The volume of a cylinder is represented by the formula $V = \pi r^2 h$.

Find each missing height and show your reasoning.

volume (cubic inches)	radius (inches)	height (inches)
96π	4	
31.25π	2.5	
V	r	

(From Unit 2, Lesson 9.)

8. Match each equation with the slope m and y-intercept of its graph.

A. $m = $ -6, y-int $= (0, 12)$

B. $m = $ -6, y-int $= (0, 5)$

C. $m = -\frac{5}{6}$, y-int $= (0, 1)$

D. $m = \frac{5}{6}$, y-int $= (0, 1)$

E. $m = \frac{5}{6}$, y-int $= (0, -1)$

F. $m = \frac{5}{6}$, y-int $= (0, $ -5$)$

1. $5x - 6y = 30$

2. $y = 5 - 6x$

3. $y = \frac{5}{6}x + 1$

4. $5x - 6y = 6$

5. $5x + 6y = 6$

6. $6x + y = 12$

(From Unit 2, Lesson 11.)

9. Solve each system of equations.

a. $\begin{cases} 2x + 3y = 4 \\ 2x = 7y + 24 \end{cases}$

b. $\begin{cases} 5x + 3y = 23 \\ 3y = 15x - 21 \end{cases}$

(From Unit 2, Lesson 13.)

10. Elena and Kiran are playing a board game. After one round, Elena says, "You earned so many more points than I did. If you earned 5 more points, your score would be twice mine!"

Kiran says, "Oh, I don't think I did that much better. I only scored 9 points higher than you did."

a. Write a system of equations to represent each student's comment. Be sure to specify what your variables represent.

b. If both students were correct, how many points did each student score? Show your reasoning.

(From Unit 2, Lesson 13.)

Lesson 15: Solving Systems by Elimination (Part 2)

- Let's think about why adding and subtracting equations works for solving systems of linear equations.

15.1: Is It Still True?

Here is an equation: $50 + 1 = 51$.

1. Perform each of the following operations and answer these questions: What does each resulting equation look like? Is it still a true equation?

   a. Add 12 to each side of the equation.

   b. Add $10 + 2$ to the left side of the equation and 12 to the right side.

   c. Add the equation $4 + 3 = 7$ to the equation $50 + 1 = 51$.

2. Write a new equation that, when added to $50 + 1 = 51$, gives a sum that is also a true equation.

3. Write a new equation that, when added to $50 + 1 = 51$, gives a sum that is a false equation.

15.2: Classroom Supplies

A teacher purchased 20 calculators and 10 measuring tapes for her class and paid $495. Later, she realized that she didn't order enough supplies. She placed another order of 8 of the same calculators and 1 more of the same measuring tape and paid $178.50.

This system represents the constraints in this situation:

$$\begin{cases} 20c + 10m = 495 \\ 8c + m = 178.50 \end{cases}$$

1. Discuss with a partner:

   a. In this situation, what do the solutions to the first equation mean?

   b. What do the solutions to the second equation mean?

   c. For each equation, how many possible solutions are there? Explain how you know.

   d. In this situation, what does the solution to the system mean?

2. Find the solution to the system. Explain or show your reasoning.

3. To be reimbursed for the cost of the supplies, the teacher recorded: "Items purchased: 28 calculators and 11 measuring tapes. Amount: $673.50."

   a. Write an equation to represent the relationship between the numbers of calculators and measuring tapes, the prices of those supplies, and the total amount spent.

   b. How is this equation related to the first two equations?

   c. In this situation, what do the solutions of this equation mean?

d. How many possible solutions does this equation have? How many solutions make sense in this situation? Explain your reasoning.

15.3: A Bunch of Systems

Solve each system of equations without graphing and show your reasoning. Then, check your solutions.

A $\begin{cases} 2x + 3y = 7 \\ -2x + 4y = 14 \end{cases}$

B $\begin{cases} 2x + 3y = 7 \\ 3x - 3y = 3 \end{cases}$

C $\begin{cases} 2x + 3y = 5 \\ 2x + 4y = 9 \end{cases}$

D $\begin{cases} 2x + 3y = 16 \\ 6x - 5y = 20 \end{cases}$

Are you ready for more?

This system has three equations: $\begin{cases} 3x + 2y - z = 7 \\ -3x + y + 2z = -14 \\ 3x + y - z = 10 \end{cases}$

1. Add the first two equations to get a new equation.

2. Add the second two equations to get a new equation.

3. Solve the system of your two new equations.

4. What is the solution to the original system of equations?

Lesson 15 Summary

When solving a system with two equations, why is it acceptable to add the two equations, or to subtract one equation from the other?

Remember that an equation is a statement that says two things are equal. For example, the equation $a = b$ says a number a has the same value as another number b. The equation $10 + 2 = 12$ says that $10 + 2$ has the same value as 12.

If $a = b$ and $10 + 2 = 12$ are true statements, then adding $10 + 2$ to a and adding 12 to b means adding the same amount to each side of $a = b$. The result, $a + 10 + 2 = b + 12$, is also a true statement.

As long as we add an equal amount to each side of a true equation, the two sides of the resulting equation will remain equal.

We can reason the same way about adding variable equations in a system like this:

$\begin{cases} e + f = 17 \\ -2e + f = -1 \end{cases}$

In each equation, if (e, f) is a solution, the expression on the left of the equal sign and the number on the right are equal. Because $-2e + f$ is equal to -1:

- Adding $-2e + f$ to $e + f$ and adding -1 to 17 means adding an equal amount to each side of $e + f = 17$. The two sides of the new equation, $-e + 2f = 16$, stay equal.

$$\begin{array}{r} e + f = 17 \\ -2e + f = -1 \quad + \\ \hline -e + 2f = 16 \end{array}$$

The e- and f-values that make the original equations true also make this equation true.

- Subtracting $-2e + f$ from $e + f$ and subtracting -1 from 17 means subtracting an equal amount from each side of $e + f = 17$. The two sides of the new equation, $3e = 18$, stay equal.

$$\begin{array}{r} e + f = 17 \\ -2e + f = -1 \quad - \\ \hline 3e \quad\quad = 18 \end{array}$$

The f-variable is eliminated, but the e-value that makes both the original equations true also makes this equation true.

From $3e = 18$, we know that $e = 6$. Because 6 is also the e-value that makes the original equations true, we can substitute it into one of the equations and find the f-value.

The solution to the system is $e = 6$, $f = 11$, or the point $(6, 11)$ on the graphs representing the system. If we substitute 6 and 11 for e and f in any of the equations, we will find true equations. (Try it!)

Lesson 15 Practice Problems

1. Solve this system of linear equations without graphing: $\begin{cases} 5x + 4y = 8 \\ 10x - 4y = 46 \end{cases}$

2. Select **all** the equations that share a solution with this system of equations.

$\begin{cases} 5x + 4y = 24 \\ 2x - 7y = 26 \end{cases}$

   A. $7x + 3y = 50$

   B. $7x - 3y = 50$

   C. $5x + 4y = 2x - 7y$

   D. $3x - 11y = \text{-}2$

   E. $3x + 11y = \text{-}2$

3. Students performed in a play on a Friday and a Saturday. For both performances, adult tickets cost a dollars each and student tickets cost s dollars each.

   On Friday, they sold 125 adult tickets and 65 student tickets, and collected $1,200. On Saturday, they sold 140 adult tickets and 50 student tickets, and collect $1,230.

   This situation is represented by this system of equations: $\begin{cases} 125a + 65s = 1{,}200 \\ 140a + 50s = 1{,}230 \end{cases}$

   a. What could the equation $265a + 115s = 2{,}430$ mean in this situation?

   b. The solution to the original system is the pair $a = 7$ and $s = 5$. Explain why it makes sense that this pair of values is also the solution to the equation $265a + 115s = 2{,}430$.

4. Which statement explains why $13x - 13y = -26$ shares a solution with this system of equations: $\begin{cases} 10x - 3y = 29 \\ -3x + 10y = 55 \end{cases}$

    A. Because $13x - 13y = -26$ is the product of the two equations in the system of equations, it the must share a solution with the system of equations.

    B. The three equations all have the same slope but different y-intercepts. Equations with the same slope but different y-intercepts always share a solution.

    C. Because $10x - 3y$ is equal to 29, I can add $10x - 3y$ to the left side of $-3x + 10y = 55$ and add 29 to the right side of the same equation. Adding equivalent expressions to each side of an equation does not change the solution to the equation.

    D. Because $-3x + 10y$ is equal to 55, I can subtract $-3x + 10y$ from the left side of $10x - 3y = 29$ and subtract 55 from its right side. Subtracting equivalent expressions from each side of an equation does not change the solution to the equation.

5. Select **all** equations that can result from adding these two equations or subtracting one from the other. $\begin{cases} x + y = 12 \\ 3x - 5y = 4 \end{cases}$

    A. $-2x - 4y = 8$

    B. $-2x + 6y = 8$

    C. $4x - 4y = 16$

    D. $4x + 4y = 16$

    E. $2x - 6y = -8$

    F. $5x - 4y = 28$

(From Unit 2, Lesson 14.)

6. Solve each system of equations.

a. $\begin{cases} 7x - 12y = 180 \\ 7x = 84 \end{cases}$

b. $\begin{cases} -16y = 4x \\ 4x + 27y = 11 \end{cases}$

(From Unit 2, Lesson 13.)

7. Here is a system of equations: $\begin{cases} 7x - 4y = \text{-}11 \\ 7x + 4y = \text{-}59 \end{cases}$

Would you rather use subtraction or addition to solve the system? Explain your reasoning.

(From Unit 2, Lesson 14.)

8. The box plot represents the distribution of the number of free throws that 20 students made out of 10 attempts.

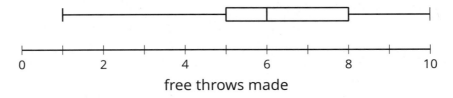

free throws made

After reviewing the data, the value recorded as 1 is determined to have been an error. The box plot represents the distribution of the same data set, but with the minimum, 1, removed.

free throws made

The median is 6 free throws for both plots.

   a. Explain why the median remains the same when 1 was removed from the data set.

   b. When 1 is removed from the data set, does the mean remain the same? Explain your reasoning.

(From Unit 1, Lesson 10.)

9. In places where there are crickets, the outdoor temperature can be predicted by the rate at which crickets chirp. One equation that models the relationship between chirps and outdoor temperature is $f = \frac{1}{4}c + 40$, where c is the number of chirps per minute and f is the temperature in degrees Fahrenheit.

   a. Suppose 110 chirps are heard in a minute. According to this model, what is the outdoor temperature?

   b. If it is $75° F$ outside, about how many chirps can we expect to hear in one minute?

   c. The equation is only a good model of the relationship when the outdoor temperature is at least $55° F$. (Below that temperature, crickets aren't around or inclined to chirp.) How many chirps can we expect to hear in a minute at that temperature?

   d. On the coordinate plane, draw a graph that represents the relationship between the number of chirps and the temperature.

   e. Explain what the coefficient $\frac{1}{4}$ in the equation tells us about the relationship.

   f. Explain what the 40 in the equation tells us about the relationship.

   (From Unit 2, Lesson 10.)

Lesson 16: Solving Systems by Elimination (Part 3)

- Let's find out how multiplying equations by a factor can help us solve systems of linear equations.

16.1: Multiplying Equations By a Number

Consider two equations in a system:

$$\begin{cases} 4x + \ y = \ 1 & \text{Equation A} \\ \ x + 2y = \ 9 & \text{Equation B} \end{cases}$$

1. Use graphing technology to graph the equations. Then, identify the coordinates of the solution.

2. Write a few equations that are equivalent to equation A by multiplying both sides of it by the same number, for example, 2, -5, or $\frac{1}{2}$. Let's call the resulting equations A1, A2, and A3. Record your equations here:

   a. Equation A1:

   b. Equation A2:

   c. Equation A3:

3. Graph the equations you generated. Make a couple of observations about the graphs.

16.2: Writing a New System to Solve a Given System

Here is a system you solved by graphing earlier.

$$\begin{cases} 4x + \ y = \ 1 & \text{Equation A} \\ \ x + 2y = \ 9 & \text{Equation B} \end{cases}$$

To start solving the system, Elena wrote:

$$4x + \ y = \ 1$$
$$4x + 8y = 36$$

And then she wrote:

$$4x + y = 1$$
$$4x + 8y = 36 \quad -$$
$$\overline{}$$
$$-7y = -35$$

1. What were Elena's first two moves? What might be possible reasons for those moves?

2. Complete the solving process algebraically. Show that the solution is indeed $x = -1, y = 5$.

16.3: What Comes Next?

Your teacher will give you some slips of paper with systems of equations written on them. Each system represents a step in solving this system:

$$\begin{cases} \frac{4}{5}x + 6y = 15 \\ -x + 18y = 11 \end{cases}$$

Arrange the slips in the order that would lead to a solution. Be prepared to:

• Describe what move takes one system to the next system.

• Explain why each system is equivalent to the one before it.

Are you ready for more?

This system of equations has solution (5, -2): $\begin{cases} Ax - By = 24 \\ Bx + Ay = 31 \end{cases}$

Find the missing values A and B.

16.4: Build Some Equivalent Systems

Here is a system of equations:

$$\begin{cases} 12a + 5b = \text{-}15 \\ 8a + b = 11 \end{cases}$$

1. To solve this system, Diego wrote these equivalent systems for his first two steps.

   Step 1:

   $$\begin{cases} 12a + 5b = \text{-}15 \\ \text{-}40a + \text{-}5b = \text{-}55 \end{cases}$$

   Step 2:

   $$\begin{cases} 12a + 5b = \text{-}15 \\ \text{-}28a = \text{-}70 \end{cases}$$

   Describe the move that Diego made to get each equivalent system. Be prepared to explain how you know the systems in Step 1 and Step 2 have the same solution as the original system.

2. Write another set of equivalent systems (different than Diego's first two steps) that will allow one variable to be eliminated and enable you to solve the original system. Be prepared to describe the moves you make to create each new system and to explain why each one has the same solution as the original system.

3. Use your equivalent systems to solve the original system. Then, check your solution by substituting the pair of values into the original system.

Lesson 16 Summary

We now have two algebraic strategies for solving systems of equations: by substitution and by elimination. In some systems, the equations may give us a clue as to which strategy to use. For example:

$$\begin{cases} y = 2x - 11 \\ 3x + 2y = 18 \end{cases}$$

In this system, y is already isolated in one equation. We can solve the system by substituting $2x - 11$ for y in the second equation and finding x.

$$\begin{cases} 3x - y = \text{-}17 \\ \text{-}3x + 4y = 23 \end{cases}$$

This system is set up nicely for elimination because of the opposite coefficients of the x-variable. Adding the two equations eliminates x so we can solve for y.

In other systems, which strategy to use is less straightforward, either because no variables are isolated, or because no variables have equal or opposite coefficients. For example:

$$\begin{cases} 2x + 3y = 15 \\ 3x - 9y = 18 \end{cases}$$

Equation A

Equation B

To solve this system by elimination, we first need to rewrite one or both equations so that one variable can be eliminated. To do that, we can multiply both sides of an equation by the same factor. Remember that doing this doesn't change the equality of the two sides of the equation, so the x- and y-values that make the first equation true also make the new equation true.

There are different ways to eliminate a variable with this approach. For instance, we could:

- Multiply Equation A by 3 to get $6x + 9y = 45$. Adding this equation to Equation B eliminates y.

$$\begin{cases} 6x + 9y = 45 \\ 3x - 9y = 18 \end{cases}$$

Equation A1

Equation B

- Multiply Equation B by $\frac{2}{3}$ to get $2x - 6y = 12$. Subtracting this equation from Equation A eliminates x.

$$\begin{cases} 2x + 3y = 15 \\ 2x - 6y = 12 \end{cases}$$

Equation A

Equation B1

- Multiply Equation A by $\frac{1}{2}$ to get $x + \frac{3}{2}y = 7\frac{1}{2}$ and multiply Equation B by $\frac{1}{3}$ to get $x - 3y = 6$. Subtracting one equation from the other eliminates x.

$$\begin{cases} x + \dfrac{3}{2}y = 7\dfrac{1}{2} \\ x - 3y = 6 \end{cases}$$

Equation A2

Equation B2

Each multiple of an original equation is equivalent to the original equation. So each new pair of equations is equivalent to the original system and has the same solution.

Let's solve the original system using the first equivalent system we found earlier.

$$\begin{cases} 6x + 9y = 45 & \text{Equation A1} \\ 3x - 9y = 18 & \text{Equation B} \end{cases}$$

- Adding the two equations eliminates y, leaving a new equation $9x = 63$, or $x = 7$.

$$\begin{aligned} 6x + 9y &= 45 \\ 3x - 9y &= 18 \quad + \\ \hline 9x + 0 &= 63 \\ x &= 7 \end{aligned}$$

- Putting together $x = 7$ and the original $3x - 9y = 18$ gives us another equivalent system.

$$\begin{cases} x = 7 \\ 3x - 9y = 18 \end{cases}$$

- Substituting 7 for x in the second equation allows us to solve for y.

$$\begin{aligned} 3(7) - 9y &= 18 \\ 21 - 9y &= 18 \\ -9y &= -3 \\ y &= \frac{1}{3} \end{aligned}$$

When we solve a system by elimination, we are essentially writing a series of **equivalent systems**, or systems with the same solution. Each equivalent system gets us closer and closer to the solution of the original system.

$$\begin{cases} 2x + 3y = 15 \\ 3x - 9y = 18 \end{cases} \qquad \begin{cases} 6x + 9y = 45 \\ 3x - 9y = 18 \end{cases} \qquad \begin{cases} x = 7 \\ 3x - 9y = 18 \end{cases} \qquad \begin{cases} x = 7 \\ y = \frac{1}{3} \end{cases}$$

Glossary

- equivalent systems

Lesson 16 Practice Problems

1. Solve each system of equations.

   a. $\begin{cases} 2x - 4y = 10 \\ x + 5y = 40 \end{cases}$

   b. $\begin{cases} 3x - 5y = 4 \\ \text{-}2x + 6y = 18 \end{cases}$

2. Tyler is solving this system of equations: $\begin{cases} 4p + 2q = 62 \\ 8p - q = 59 \end{cases}$

   He can think of two ways to eliminate a variable and solve the system:

   ◦ Multiply $4p + 2q = 62$ by 2, then subtract $8p - q = 59$ from the result.

   ◦ Multiply $8p - q = 59$ by 2, then add the result to $4p + 2q = 62$.

   Do both strategies work for solving the system? Explain or show your reasoning.

3. Andre and Elena are solving this system of equations: $\begin{cases} y = 3x \\ y = 9x - 30 \end{cases}$

    ○ Andre's first step is to write: $3x = 9x - 30$

    ○ Elena's first step is to create a new system: $\begin{cases} 3y = 9x \\ y = 9x - 30 \end{cases}$

Do you agree with either first step? Explain your reasoning.

4. Select **all** systems that are equivalent to this system: $\begin{cases} 6d + 4.5e = 16.5 \\ 5d + 0.5e = 4 \end{cases}$

A. $\begin{cases} 6d + 4.5e = 16.5 \\ 45d + 4.5e = 4 \end{cases}$

B. $\begin{cases} 30d + 22.5e = 82.5 \\ 5d + 0.5e = 4 \end{cases}$

C. $\begin{cases} 30d + 22.5e = 82.5 \\ 30d + 3e = 24 \end{cases}$

D. $\begin{cases} 6d + 4.5e = 16.5 \\ 6d + 0.6e = 4.8 \end{cases}$

E. $\begin{cases} 12d + 9e = 33 \\ 10d + 0.5e = 8 \end{cases}$

F. $\begin{cases} 6d + 4.5e = 16.5 \\ 11d + 5e = 20.5 \end{cases}$

5. Here is a system of equations with a solution: $\begin{cases} p + 8q = \text{-}8 \\ \dfrac{1}{2}p + 5q = \text{-}5 \end{cases}$

   a. Write a system of equations that is equivalent to this system. Describe what you did to the original system to get the new system.

   b. Explain how you know the new system has the same solution as the original system.

6. The cost to mail a package is $5.00. Noah has postcard stamps that are worth $0.34 each and first-class stamps that are worth $0.49 each.

   a. Write an equation that relates the number of postcard stamps p, the number of first-class stamps f, and the cost of mailing the package.

   b. Solve the equation for f.

   c. Solve the equation for p.

   d. If Noah puts 7 first-class stamps on the package, how many postcard stamps will he need?

   (From Unit 2, Lesson 8.)

7. Here is a system of linear equations: $\begin{cases} 2x + 7y = 8 \\ y + 2x = 14 \end{cases}$

   Find at least one way to solve the system by substitution and show your reasoning. How many ways can you find? (Regardless of the substitution that you do, the solution should be the same.)

   (From Unit 2, Lesson 13.)

8. Here is a system of equations: $\begin{cases} -7x + 3y = -65 \\ -7x + 10y = -135 \end{cases}$

   Write an equation that results from subtracting the two equations.

   (From Unit 2, Lesson 14.)

9. A grocery store sells bananas for b dollars a pound and grapes for g dollars a pound. Priya buys 2.2 pounds of bananas and 3.6 pounds of grapes for $9.35. Andre buys 1.6 pounds of bananas and 1.2 pounds of grapes for $3.68.

   This situation is represented by the system of equations: $\begin{cases} 2.2b + 3.6g = 9.35 \\ 1.6b + 1.2g = 3.68 \end{cases}$

   Explain why it makes sense in this situation that the solution of this system is also a solution to $3.8b + 4.8g = 13.03$.

   (From Unit 2, Lesson 15.)

Lesson 17: Systems of Linear Equations and Their Solutions

- Let's find out how many solutions a system of equations could have.

17.1: A Curious System

Andre is trying to solve this system of equations: $\begin{cases} x + y = 3 \\ 4x = 12 - 4y \end{cases}$

Looking at the first equation, he thought, "The solution to the system is a pair of numbers that add up to 3. I wonder which two numbers they are."

1. Choose any two numbers that add up to 3. Let the first one be the x-value and the second one be the y-value.

2. The pair of values you chose is a solution to the first equation. Check if it is also a solution to the second equation. Then, pause for a brief discussion with your group.

3. How many solutions does the system have? Use what you know about equations or about solving systems to show that you are right.

17.2: What's the Deal?

A recreation center is offering special prices on its pool passes and gym memberships for the summer. On the first day of the offering, a family paid $96 for 4 pool passes and 2 gym memberships. Later that day, an individual bought a pool pass for herself, a pool pass for a friend, and 1 gym membership. She paid $72.

1. Write a system of equations that represents the relationships between pool passes, gym memberships, and the costs. Be sure to state what each variable represents.

2. Find the price of a pool pass and the price of a gym membership by solving the system algebraically. Explain or show your reasoning.

3. Use graphing technology to graph the equations in the system. Make 1-2 observations about your graphs.

17.3: Card Sort: Sorting Systems

Your teacher will give you a set of cards. Each card contains a system of equations.

Sort the systems into three groups based on the number of solutions each system has. Be prepared to explain how you know where each system belongs.

Are you ready for more?

1. In the cards, for each system with no solution, change a single constant term so that there are infinitely many solutions to the system.

2. For each system with infinitely many solutions, change a single constant term so that there are no solutions to the system.

3. Explain why in these situations it is impossible to change a single constant term so that there is exactly one solution to the system.

17.4: One, Zero, Infinitely Many

Here is an equation: $5x - 2y = 10$.

Create a second equation that would make a system of equations with:

1. One solution

2. No solutions

3. Infinitely many solutions

Lesson 17 Summary

We have seen many examples of a system where one pair of values satisfies both equations. Not all systems, however, have one solution. Some systems have many solutions, and others have no solutions.

Let's look at three systems of equations and their graphs.

System 1: $\begin{cases} 3x + 4y = 8 \\ 3x - 4y = 8 \end{cases}$

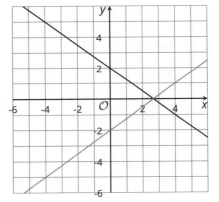

The graphs of the equations in System 1 intersect at one point. The coordinates of the point are the one pair of values that are simultaneously true for both equations. When we solve the equations, we get exactly one solution.

System 2: $\begin{cases} 3x + 4y = 8 \\ 6x + 8y = 16 \end{cases}$

The graphs of the equations in System 2 appear to be the same line. This suggests that every point on the line is a solution to both equations, or that the system has infinitely many solutions.

System 3: $\begin{cases} 3x + 4y = 8 \\ 3x + 4y = \text{-}4 \end{cases}$

The graphs of the equations in System 3 appear to be parallel. If the lines never intersect, then there is no common point that is a solution to both equations and the system has no solutions.

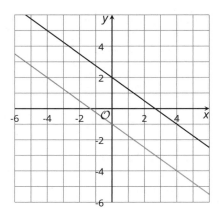

How can we tell, without graphing, that System 2 indeed has many solutions?

- Notice that $3x + 4y = 8$ and $6x + 8y = 16$ are equivalent equations. Multiplying the first equation by 2 gives the second equation. Multiplying the second equation by $\frac{1}{2}$ gives the first equation. This means that any solution to the first equation is a solution to the second.

- Rearranging $3x + 4y = 8$ into slope-intercept form gives $y = \dfrac{8 - 3x}{4}$, or $y = 2 - \frac{3}{4}x$. Rearranging $6x + 8y = 16$ gives $y = \dfrac{16 - 6y}{8}$, which is also $y = 2 - \frac{3}{4}x$. Both lines have the same slope and the same y-value for the vertical intercept!

How can we tell, without graphing, that System 3 has no solutions?

- Notice that in one equation $3x + 4y$ equals 8, but in the other equation it equals -4. Because it is impossible for the same expression to equal 8 and -4, there must not be a pair of x- and y-values that are simultaneously true for both equations. This tells us that the system has no solutions.

- Rearranging each equation into slope-intercept form gives $y = 2 - \frac{3}{4}x$ and $y = \text{-}1 - \frac{3}{4}x$. The two graphs have the same slope but the y-values of their vertical intercepts are different. This tells us that the lines are parallel and will never cross.

Lesson 17 Practice Problems

1. Here is a system of equations: $\begin{cases} 3x - y = 17 \\ x + 4y = 10 \end{cases}$

   a. Solve the system by graphing the equations (by hand or using technology).

   b. Explain how you could tell, without graphing, that there is only one solution to the system.

2. Consider this system of linear equations: $\begin{cases} y = \frac{4}{5}x - 3 \\ y = \frac{4}{5}x + 1 \end{cases}$

   a. Without graphing, determine how many solutions you would expect this system of equations to have. Explain your reasoning.

   b. Try solving the system of equations algebraically and describe the result that you get. Does it match your prediction?

3. How many solutions does this system of equations have? Explain how you know.

$$\begin{cases} 9x - 3y = -6 \\ 5y = 15x + 10 \end{cases}$$

4. Select **all** systems of equations that have no solutions.

A. $\begin{cases} y = 5 - 3x \\ y = \text{-}3x + 4 \end{cases}$

B. $\begin{cases} y = 4x - 1 \\ 4y = 16x - 4 \end{cases}$

C. $\begin{cases} 5x - 2y = 3 \\ 10x - 4y = 6 \end{cases}$

D. $\begin{cases} 3x + 7y = 42 \\ 6x + 14y = 50 \end{cases}$

E. $\begin{cases} y = 5 + 2x \\ y = 5x + 2 \end{cases}$

5. Solve each system of equations without graphing.

a. $\begin{cases} 2v + 6w = \text{-}36 \\ 5v + 2w = 1 \end{cases}$

b. $\begin{cases} 6t - 9u = 10 \\ 2t + 3u = 4 \end{cases}$

(From Unit 2, Lesson 16.)

6. Select **all** the dot plots that appear to contain outliers.

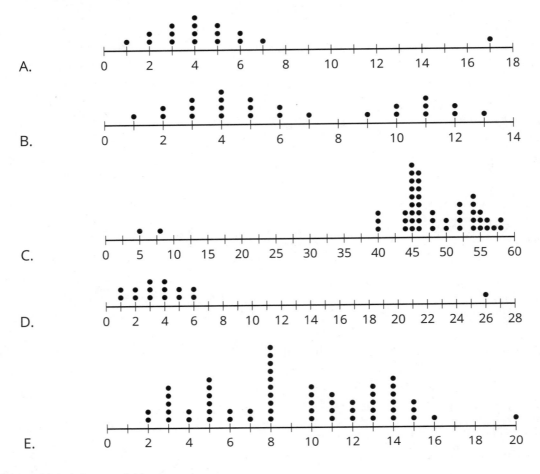

A.

B.

C.

D.

E.

(From Unit 1, Lesson 14.)

Algebra 1 iM KH

7. Here is a system of equations: $\begin{cases} -x + 6y = 9 \\ x + 6y = -3 \end{cases}$

Would you rather use subtraction or addition to solve the system? Explain your reasoning.

(From Unit 2, Lesson 14.)

8. Here is a system of linear equations: $\begin{cases} 6x - y = 18 \\ 4x + 2y = 26 \end{cases}$

Select **all** the steps that would help to eliminate a variable and enable solving.

A. Multiply the first equation by 2, then subtract the second equation from the result.

B. Multiply the first equation by 4 and the second equation by 6, then subtract the resulting equations.

C. Multiply the first equation by 2, then add the result to the second equation.

D. Divide the second equation by 2, then add the result to the first equation.

E. Multiply the second equation by 6, then subtract the result from the first equation.

(From Unit 2, Lesson 16.)

9. Consider this system of equations, which has one solution: $\begin{cases} 2x + 2y = 180 \\ 0.1x + 7y = 78 \end{cases}$

Here are some equivalent systems. Each one is a step in solving the original system.

Step 1:

$$\begin{cases} 7x + 7y = 630 \\ 0.1x + 7y = 78 \end{cases}$$

Step 2:

$$\begin{cases} 6.9x = 552 \\ 0.1x + 7y = 78 \end{cases}$$

Step 3:

$$\begin{cases} x = 80 \\ 0.1x + 7y = 78 \end{cases}$$

   a. Look at the original system and the system in Step 1.

      i. What was done to the original system to get the system in Step 1?

      ii. Explain why the system in Step 1 shares a solution with the original system.

   b. Look at the system in Step 1 and the system in Step 2.

      i. What was done to the system in Step 1 to get the system in Step 2?

      ii. Explain why the system in Step 2 shares a solution with that in Step 1.

   c. What is the solution to the original system?

   (From Unit 2, Lesson 16.)

Lesson 18: Representing Situations with Inequalities

- Let's use inequalities to represent constraints in situations.

18.1: What Do Those Symbols Mean?

1. Match each inequality to the meaning of a symbol within it.

   a. $h > 50$ ○ less than or equal to

   b. $h \leq 20$ ○ greater than

   c. $30 \geq h$ ○ greater than or equal to

2. Is 25 a solution to any of the inequalities? Which one(s)?

3. Is 40 a solution to any of the inequalities? Which one(s)?

4. Is 30 a solution to any of the inequalities? Which one(s)?

18.2: Planning the Senior Ball

Seniors in a student council of a high school are trying to come up with a budget for the Senior Ball. Here is some information they have gathered:

- Last year, 120 people attended. It was a success and is expected to be even bigger this year. Anywhere up to 200 people might attend.

- There needs to be at least 1 chaperone for every 20 students.

- The ticket price can not exceed $20 per person.

- The revenue from ticket sales needs to cover the cost of the meals and entertainment, and also make a profit of at least $200 to be contributed to the school.

Here are some inequalities the seniors wrote about the situation. Each letter stands for one quantity in the situation. Determine what is meant by each letter.

- $t \leq 20$

- $120 \leq p \leq 200$

- $pt - m \geq 200$

- $c \geq \frac{p}{20}$

Are you ready for more?

Kiran says we should add the constraint $t \geq 0$.

1. What is the reasoning behind this constraint?

2. What other "natural constraint" like this should be added?

18.3: Elevator Constraints

An elevator car in a skyscraper can hold at most 15 people. For safety reasons, each car can carry a maximum of 1,500 kg. On average, an adult weighs 70 kg and a child weighs 35 kg. Assume that each person carries 4 kg of gear with them.

1. Write as many equations and inequalities as you can think of to represent the constraints in this situation. Be sure to specify the meaning of any letters that you use. (Avoid using the letters z, m, or g.)

2. Trade your work with a partner and read each other's equations and inequalities.

   a. Explain to your partner what you think their statements mean, and listen to their explanation of yours.

   b. Make adjustments to your equations and inequalities so that they are communicated more clearly.

3. Rewrite your equations and inequalities so that they would work for a different building where:

   ○ an elevator car can hold at most z people

   ○ each car can carry a maximum of m kilograms

   ○ each person carries g kg of gear

Lesson 18 Summary

We have used equations and the equal sign to represent relationships and constraints in various situations. Not all relationships and constraints involve equality, however.

In some situations, one quantity is, or needs to be, greater than or less than another. To describe these situations, we can use inequalities and symbols such as $<, \leq, >$, or $\geq$.

When working with inequalities, it helps to remember what the symbol means, in words. For example:

- $100 < a$ means "100 is less than a."

- $y \leq 55$ means "y is less than or equal to 55," or "y is not more than 55."

- $20 > 18$ means "20 is greater than 18."

- $t \geq 40$ means "t is greater than or equal to 40," or "t is at least 40."

These inequalities are fairly straightforward. Each inequality states the relationship between two numbers ($20 > 18$), or they describe the limit or boundary of a quantity in terms of a number ($100 < a$).

Inequalities can also express relationships or constraints that are more complex. Here are some examples:

- The area of a rectangle, A, with a length of 4 meters and a width w meters is no more than 100 square meters.
  $$A \leq 100$$
  $$4w \leq 100$$

- To cover all the expenses of a musical production each week, the number of weekday tickets sold, d, and the number of weekend tickets sold, e, must be greater than 4,000.
  $$d + e > 4{,}000$$

- Elena would like the number of hours she works in a week, h, to be more than 5 but no more than 20.
  $$h > 5$$
  $$h \leq 20$$

- The total cost, T, of buying a adult shirts and c child shirts must be less than 150. Adult shirts are \$12 each and children shirts are \$7 each.
  $$T < 150$$
  $$12a + 7c < 150$$

In upcoming lessons, we'll use inequalities to help us solve problems.

Lesson 18 Practice Problems

1. Tyler goes to the store. His budget is $125. Which inequality represents x, the amount in dollars Tyler can spend at the store?

   A. $x \leq 125$

   B. $x \geq 125$

   C. $x > 125$

   D. $x < 125$

2. Jada is making lemonade for a get-together with her friends. She expects a total of 5 to 8 people to be there (including herself). She plans to prepare 2 cups of lemonade for each person.

   The lemonade recipe calls for 4 scoops of lemonade powder for each quart of water. Each quart is equivalent to 4 cups.

   Let n represent the number of people at the get-together, c the number of cups of water, ℓ the number of scoops of lemonade powder.

   Select **all** the mathematical statements that represent the quantities and constraints in the situation.

   A. $5 < n < 8$

   B. $5 \leq n \leq 8$

   C. $c = 2n$

   D. $\ell = c$

   E. $10 < c < 16$

   F. $10 \leq \ell \leq 16$

3. A doctor sees between 7 and 12 patients each day. On Mondays and Tuesdays, the appointment times are 15 minutes. On Wednesdays and Thursdays, they are 30 minutes. On Fridays, they are one hour long. The doctor works for no more than 8 hours a day.

Here are some inequalities that represent this situation.

$$0.25 \leq y \leq 1 \qquad\qquad 7 \leq x \leq 12 \qquad\qquad xy \leq 8$$

    a. What does each variable represent?

    b. What does the expression xy in the last inequality mean in this situation?

4. Han wants to build a dog house. He makes a list of the materials needed:

- At least 60 square feet of plywood for the surfaces

- At least 36 feet of wood planks for the frame of the dog house

- Between 1 and 2 quarts of paint

Han's budget is $65. Plywood costs $0.70 per square foot, planks of wood cost $0.10 per foot, and paint costs $8 per quart.

Write inequalities to represent the material constraints and cost contraints in this situation. Be sure to specify what your variables represent.

5. The equation $V = \frac{1}{3}\pi r^2 h$ represents the volume of a cone, where r is the radius of the cone and h is the height of the cone.

Which equation is solved for the height of the cone?

A. $h = V - \pi r^2$

B. $h = \frac{1}{3}\pi r^2 V$

C. $3V - \pi r^2 = h$

D. $h = \dfrac{3V}{\pi r^2}$

(From Unit 2, Lesson 9.)

6. Solve each system of equations without graphing.

a. $\begin{cases} 2x + 3y = 5 \\ 2x + 4y = 9 \end{cases}$

b. $\begin{cases} \frac{2}{3}x + y = \frac{7}{3} \\ \frac{2}{3}x - y = 1 \end{cases}$

(From Unit 2, Lesson 14.)

7. There is a pair of x and y values that make each equation true in this system of equations: $\begin{cases} 5x + 3y = 8 \\ 4x + 7y = 34 \end{cases}$

Explain why the same pair of values also make $9x + 10y = 42$ true.

(From Unit 2, Lesson 15.)

8. Which ordered pair is a solution to this system of equations? $\begin{cases} 7x + 5y = 59 \\ 3x - 9y = 159 \end{cases}$

   A. $(-17, -12)$

   B. $(-17, 12)$

   C. $(17, -12)$

   D. $(17, 12)$

(From Unit 2, Lesson 16.)

9. Which equation has exactly one solution in common with the equation $y = 6x - 2$?

   A. $18x - 3y = 6$

   B. $\frac{1}{2}y = 3x - 2$

   C. $2y = 4x - 12$

   D. $18x - 12 = 3y$

(From Unit 2, Lesson 17.)

10. How many solutions does this system of equations have? Explain how you know.

$$\begin{cases} y = \text{-}4x + 3 \\ 2x + 8y = 10 \end{cases}$$

(From Unit 2, Lesson 17.)

Lesson 19: Solutions to Inequalities in One Variable

- Let's find and interpret solutions to inequalities in one variable.

19.1: Find a Value, Any Value

1. Write some solutions to the inequality $y \leq 9.2$. Be prepared to explain what makes a value a solution to this inequality.

2. Write one solution to the inequality $7(3 - x) > 14$. Be prepared to explain your reasoning.

19.2: Off to an Orchard

A teacher is choosing between two options for a class field trip to an orchard.

- At Orchard A, admission costs $9 per person and 3 chaperones are required.

- At Orchard B, the cost is $10 per person, but only 1 chaperone is required.

- At each orchard, the same price applies to both chaperones and students.

1. Which orchard would be cheaper to visit if the class has:

   a. 8 students?

   b. 12 students?

   c. 30 students?

2. To help her compare the cost of her two options, the teacher first writes the equation $9(n + 3) = 10(n + 1)$, and then she writes the inequality $9(n + 3) < 10(n + 1)$.

a. What does n represent in each statement?

b. In this situation, what does the equation $9(n + 3) = 10(n + 1)$ mean?

c. What does the solution to the inequality $9(n + 3) < 10(n + 1)$ tell us?

d. Graph the solution to the inequality on the number line. Be prepared to show or explain your reasoning.

19.3: Part-Time Work

To help pay for his tuition, a college student plans to work in the evenings and on weekends. He has been offered two part-time jobs: working in the guest-services department at a hotel and waiting tables at a popular restaurant.

- The job at the hotel pays $18 an hour and offers $33 in transportation allowance per month.

- The job at the restaurant pays $7.50 an hour plus tips. The entire waitstaff typically collects about $50 in tips each hour. Tips are divided equally among the 4 waitstaff members who share a shift.

1. The equation $7.50h + \frac{50}{4}h = 18h + 33$ represents a possible constraint about a situation.

a. Solve the equation and check your solution.

b. Here is a graph on a number line.

Put a scale on the number line so that the point marked with a circle represents the solution to the equation.

2. Does one job pay better if:

   a. The student works fewer hours than the solution you found earlier? If so, which job?

   b. The student works more hours than the solution you found earlier? If so, which job?

   Be prepared to explain or show how you know.

3. Here are two inequalities and two graphs that represent the solutions to the inequalities.

   ○ Inequality 1: $7.50h + \frac{50}{4}h < 18h + 33$

   ○ Inequality 2: $7.50h + \frac{50}{4}h > 18h + 33$

   A

   B

   a. Put the same scale on each number line so that the circle represents the number of hours that you found earlier.

   b. Match each inequality with a graph that shows its solution. Be prepared to explain or show how you know.

19.4: Equality and Inequality

1. Solve this equation and check your solution: $-\dfrac{4(x+3)}{5} = 4x - 12$.

2. Consider the inequality: $-\dfrac{4(x+3)}{5} \leq 4x - 12$.

   a. Choose a couple of values less than 2 for x. Are they solutions to the inequality?

   b. Choose a couple of values greater than 2 for x. Are they solutions to the inequality?

   c. Choose 2 for x. Is it a solution?

   d. Graph the solution to the inequality on the number line.

Are you ready for more?

Here is a different type of inequality: $x^2 \leq 4$.

   1. Is 1 a solution to the inequality? Is 3 a solution? How about -3?

2. Describe all solutions to this inequality. (If you like, you can graph the solutions on a number line.)

3. Describe all solutions to the inequality $x^2 \geq 9$. Test several numbers to make sure your answer is correct.

19.5: More or Less?

Consider the inequality $-\frac{1}{2}x + 6 < 4x - 3$. Let's look at another way to find its solutions.

1. Use graphing technology to graph $y = -\frac{1}{2}x + 6$ and $y = 4x - 3$ on the same coordinate plane.

2. Use your graphs to answer the following questions:

   a. Find the values of $-\frac{1}{2}x + 6$ and $4x - 3$ when x is 1.

   b. What value of x makes $-\frac{1}{2}x + 6$ and $4x - 3$ equal?

   c. For what values of x is $-\frac{1}{2}x + 6$ less than $4x - 3$?

   d. For what values of x is $-\frac{1}{2}x + 6$ greater than $4x - 3$?

3. What is the solution to the inequality $-\frac{1}{2}x + 6 < 4x - 3$? Be prepared to explain how you know.

Lesson 19 Summary

The equation $\frac{1}{2}t = 10$ is an equation in one variable. Its solution is any value of t that makes the equation true. Only $t = 20$ meets that requirement, so 20 is the only solution.

The inequality $\frac{1}{2}t > 10$ is an inequality in one variable. Any value of t that makes the inequality true is a solution. For instance, 30 and 48 are both solutions because substituting these values for t produces true inequalities. $\frac{1}{2}(30) > 10$ is true, as is $\frac{1}{2}(48) > 10$. Because the inequality has a range of values that make it true, we sometimes refer to *all* the solutions as the **solution set**.

One way to find the solutions to an inequality is by reasoning. For example, to find the solution to $2p < 8$, we can reason that if 2 times a value is less than 8, then that value must be less than 4. So a solution to $2p < 8$ is any value of p that is less than 4.

Another way to find the solutions to $2p < 8$ is to solve the related equation $2p = 8$. In this case, dividing each side of the equation by 2 gives $p = 4$. This point, where p is 4, is the *boundary* of the solution to the inequality.

To find out the range of values that make the inequality true, we can try values less than and greater than 4 in our inequality and see which ones make a true statement.

Let's try some values less than 4:

- If $p = 3$, the inequality is $2(3) < 8$ or $6 < 8$, which is true.

- If $p = -1$, the inequality is $2(-1) < 8$ or $-2 < 8$, which is also true.

Let's try values greater than 4:

- If $p = 5$, the inequality is $2(5) < 8$ or $10 < 8$, which is false.

- If $p = 12$, the inequality is $2(12) < 8$ or $24 < 8$, which is also false.

In general, the inequality is false when p is greater than or equal to 4 and true when p is less than 4.

We can represent the solution set to an inequality by writing an inequality, $p < 4$, or by graphing on a number line. The ray pointing to the left represents all values less than 4.

Lesson 19 Practice Problems

1. Here is an inequality: $\dfrac{7x+6}{2} \le 3x + 2$

   Select **all** of the values that are a solution to the inequality.

   A. $x = -3$

   B. $x = -2$

   C. $x = -1$

   D. $x = 0$

   E. $x = 1$

   F. $x = 2$

   G. $x = 3$

2. Find the solution set to this inequality: $2x - 3 > \dfrac{2x - 5}{2}$

   A. $x < \frac{1}{2}$

   B. $x > \frac{1}{2}$

   C. $x \le \frac{1}{2}$

   D. $x \ge \frac{1}{2}$

3. Here is an inequality: $\dfrac{-10 + x}{4} + 5 \geq \dfrac{7x - 5}{3}$

What value of x will produce equality (or make the two sides equal)?

4. Noah is solving the inequality $7x + 5 > 2x + 35$. First, he solves the equation $7x + 5 = 2x + 35$ and gets $x = 6$.

How does the solution to the equation $7x + 5 = 2x + 35$ help Noah solve the inequality $7x + 5 > 2x + 35$? Explain your reasoning.

5. Which graph represents the solution to $5 + 8x < 3(2x + 4)$?

A.   -10 -9 -8 -7 -6 -5 -4 -3 -2 -1 0 1 2 3 4 5 6 7 8 9 10

B.   -10 -9 -8 -7 -6 -5 -4 -3 -2 -1 0 1 2 3 4 5 6 7 8 9 10

C.   -10 -9 -8 -7 -6 -5 -4 -3 -2 -1 0 1 2 3 4 5 6 7 8 9 10

D.   -10 -9 -8 -7 -6 -5 -4 -3 -2 -1 0 1 2 3 4 5 6 7 8 9 10

6. Solve this system of linear equations without graphing: $\begin{cases} 7x + 11y = \text{-}2 \\ 7x + 3y = 30 \end{cases}$

(From Unit 2, Lesson 15.)

7. Kiran has 27 nickels and quarters in his pocket, worth a total of $2.75.

    a. Write a system of equations to represent the relationships between the number of nickels n, the number of quarters q, and the dollar amount in this situation.

    b. How many nickels and quarters are in Kiran's pocket? Show your reasoning.

(From Unit 2, Lesson 12.)

8. How many solutions does this system of equations have? Explain how you know.

$\begin{cases} y + \frac{2}{3}x = 4 \\ 2x = 12 - 3y \end{cases}$

(From Unit 2, Lesson 17.)

9. The principal of a school is hosting a small luncheon for her staff. She plans to prepare two sandwiches for each person. Some staff members offer to bring salads and beverages.

The principal has a budget of $225 and expects at least 16 people to attend. Sandwiches cost $3 each.

Select **all** of the equations and inequalities that could represent the constraints in the situation, where n is number of people attending and s is number of sandwiches.

   A. $n \geq 16$

   B. $n \geq 32$

   C. $s < 2n$

   D. $s = 2n$

   E. $3n \leq 225$

   F. $3s \leq 225$

(From Unit 2, Lesson 18.)

10. Students at the college are allowed to work on campus no more than 20 hours per week. The jobs that are available pay different rates, starting from $8.75 an hour. Students can earn a maximum of $320 per week.

Write at least two inequalities that could represent the constraints in this situation. Be sure to specify what your variables represent.

(From Unit 2, Lesson 18.)

Lesson 20: Writing and Solving Inequalities in One Variable

- Let's solve problems by writing and solving inequalities in one variable.

20.1: Dinner for Drama Club

Kiran is getting dinner for his drama club on the evening of their final rehearsal. The budget for dinner is $60.

Kiran plans to buy some prepared dishes from a supermarket. The prepared dishes are sold by the pound, at $5.29 a pound. He also plans to buy two large bottles of sparkling water at $2.49 each.

1. Represent the constraints in the situation mathematically. If you use variables, specify what each one means.

2. How many pounds of prepared dishes can Kiran buy? Explain or show your reasoning.

20.2: Gasoline in the Tank

Han is about to mow some lawns in his neighborhood. His lawn mower has a 5-gallon fuel tank, but Han is not sure how much gasoline is in the tank.

He knows, however, that the lawn mower uses 0.4 gallon of gasoline per hour of mowing.

What are all the possible values for x, the number of hours Han can mow without refilling the lawn mower?

Write one or more inequalities to represent your response. Be prepared to explain or show your reasoning.

20.3: Different Ways of Solving

Andre and Priya used different strategies to solve the following inequality but reached the same solution.

$$2(2x + 1.5) < 18 - x$$

1. Make sense of each strategy until you can explain what each student has done.

Andre

$$2(2x + 1.5) = 18 - x$$
$$4x + 3 = 18 - x$$
$$4x - 15 = \text{-}x$$
$$\text{-}15 = \text{-}5x$$
$$3 = x$$

Testing to see if $x = 4$ is a solution:

$$2(2 \cdot 4 + 1.5) < 18 - 4$$
$$2(9.5) < 14$$
$$17 < 14$$

The inequality is false, so 4 is not a solution. If a number greater than 3 is not a solution, the solution must be less than 3, or $3 > x$.

Priya

$$2(2x + 1.5) = 18 - x$$
$$4x + 3 = 18 - x$$
$$5x + 3 = 18$$
$$5x = 15$$
$$x = 3$$

In $4x + 3 = 18 - x$, there is $4x$ on the left and $\text{-}x$ on the right.

If x is a negative number, $4x + 3$ could be positive or negative, but $18 - x$ will always be positive.

For $4x + 3 < 18 - x$ to be true, x must include negative numbers or x must be less than 3.

2. Here are four inequalities.

   a. $\frac{1}{5}p > \text{-}10$.

   b. $4(x + 7) \leq 4(2x + 8)$

   c. $\text{-}9n < 36$

   d. $\frac{c}{3} < \text{-}2(c - 7)$

Work with a partner to decide on at least two inequalities to solve. Solve one inequality using Andre's strategy (by testing values on either side the given solution), while your partner uses Priya's strategy (by reasoning about the parts of the inequality). Switch strategies for the other inequality.

Are you ready for more?

Using positive integers between 1 and 9 and each positive integer at most once, fill in values to get two constraints so that $x = 7$ is the only integer that will satisfy both constraints at the same time.

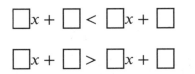

$$\square x + \square < \square x + \square$$

$$\square x + \square > \square x + \square$$

20.4: Matching Inequalities and Solutions

Match each inequality to a graph that represents its solutions. Be prepared to explain or show your reasoning.

1. $6x \leq 3x$

2. $\frac{1}{4}x > -\frac{1}{2}$

3. $5x + 4 \geq 7x$

4. $8x - 2 < -4(x - 1)$

5. $\dfrac{4x - 1}{3} > -1$

6. $\frac{12}{5} - \frac{x}{5} \leq x$

A

B

C

D

E

F

Lesson 20 Summary

Writing and solving inequalities can help us make sense of the constraints in a situation and solve problems. Let's look at an example.

Clare would like to buy a video game that costs $130. She has saved $48 so far and plans on saving $5 of her allowance each week. How many weeks, w, will it be until she has enough money to buy the game? To represent the constraints, we can write $48 + 5w \geq 130$. Let's reason about the solutions:

- Because Clare has $48 already and needs to have at least $130 to afford the game, she needs to save at least $82 more.

- If she saves $5 each week, it will take at least $\frac{82}{5}$ weeks to reach $82.

- $\frac{82}{5}$ is 16.4. Any time shorter than 16.4 weeks won't allow her to save enough.

- Assuming she saves $5 at the end of each week (instead of saving smaller amounts throughout a week), it will be at least 17 weeks before she can afford the game.

We can also solve by writing and solving a related equation to find the boundary value for w, and then determine whether the solutions are less than or greater than that value.

$$48 + 5w = 130$$
$$5w = 82$$
$$w = \frac{82}{5}$$
$$w = 16.4$$

- Substituting 16.4 for w in the original inequality gives a true statement. (When $w = 16.4$, we get $130 \geq 130$.)

- Substituting a value greater than 16.4 for w also gives a true statement. (When $w = 17$, we get $133 \geq 130$.)

- Substituting a value less than 16.4 for w gives a false statement. (When $w = 16$, we get $128 \geq 130$.)

- The solution set is therefore $w \geq 16.4$.

Sometimes the structure of an inequality can help us see whether the solutions are less than or greater than a boundary value. For example, to find the solutions to $3x > 8x$, we can solve the equation $3x = 8x$, which gives us $x = 0$. Then, instead of testing values on either side of 0, we could reason as follows about the inequality:

- If x is a positive value, then $3x$ would be less than $8x$.

- For $3x$ to be *greater* than $8x$, x must include negative values.

- For the solutions to include negative values, they must be less than 0, so the solution set would be $x < 0$.

Lesson 20 Practice Problems

1. Solve $2x < 10$. Explain how to find the solution set.

2. LIn is solving the inequality $15 - x < 14$. She knows the solution to the equation $15 - x = 14$ is $x = 1$

   How can Lin determine whether $x > 1$ or $x < 1$ is the solution to the inequality?

3. A cell phone company offers two texting plans. People who use plan A pay 10 cents for each text sent or received. People who use plan B pay 12 dollars per month, and then pay an additional 2 cents for each text sent or received.

   a. Write an inequality to represent the fact that it is cheaper for someone to use plan A than plan B. Use x to represent the number of texts they send.

   b. Solve the inequality.

4. Clare made an error when solving $-4x + 3 < 23$.

   Describe the error that she made.

   $$-4x + 3 < 23$$
   $$-4x < 20$$
   $$x < \text{-}5$$

5. Diego's goal is to walk more than 70,000 steps this week. The mean number of steps that Diego walked during the first 4 days of this week is 8,019.

   a. Write an inequality that expresses the mean number of steps that Diego needs to walk during the last 3 days of this week to walk more than 70,000 steps. Remember to define any variables that you use.

   b. If the mean number of steps Diego walks during the last 3 days of the week is 12,642, will Diego reach his goal of walking more that 70,000 steps this week?

6. Here are statistics for the length of some frog jumps in inches:

   ○ the mean is 41 inches

   ○ the median is 39 inches

   ○ the standard deviation is about 9.6 inches

   ○ the IQR is 5.5 inches

   How does each statistic change if the length of the jumps are measured in feet instead of inches?

(From Unit 1, Lesson 15.)

7. Solve this system of linear equations without graphing: $\begin{cases} 3y + 7 = 5x \\ 7x - 3y = 1 \end{cases}$

(From Unit 2, Lesson 15.)

8. Solve each system of equations without graphing.

a. $\begin{cases} 5x + 14y = \text{-}5 \\ \text{-}3x + 10y = 72 \end{cases}$

b. $\begin{cases} 20x - 5y = 289 \\ 22x + 9y = 257 \end{cases}$

(From Unit 2, Lesson 16.)

9. Noah and Lin are solving this system: $\begin{cases} 8x + 15y = 58 \\ 12x - 9y = 150 \end{cases}$

Noah multiplies the first equation by 12 and the second equation by 8, which gives:

$$\begin{cases} 96x + 180y = 696 \\ 96x - 72y = 1{,}200 \end{cases}$$

Lin says, "I know you can eliminate x by doing that and then subtracting the second equation from the first, but I can use smaller numbers. Instead of what you did, try multiplying the first equation by 6 and the second equation by 4."

a. Do you agree with Lin that her approach also works? Explain your reasoning.

b. What are the smallest whole-number factors by which you can multiply the equations in order to eliminate x?

(From Unit 2, Lesson 16.)

10. What is the solution set of the inequality $\dfrac{x+2}{2} \geq -7 - \dfrac{x}{2}$?

    A. $x \leq$ -8

    B. $x \geq$ -8

    C. $x \geq -\dfrac{9}{2}$

    D. $x \geq 8$

(From Unit 2, Lesson 19.)

Algebra 1 iM KH

Lesson 21: Graphing Linear Inequalities in Two Variables (Part 1)

- Let's find out how to use graphs to represent solutions to inequalities in two variables.

21.1: Math Talk: Less Than, Equal to, or More Than 12?

Here is an expression: $2x + 3y$.

Decide if the values in each ordered pair, (x, y), make the value of the expression less than, greater than, or equal to 12.

$(0, 5)$

$(6, 0)$

$(-1, -1)$

$(-5, 10)$

21.2: Solutions and Not Solutions

Here are four inequalities. Study each inequality assigned to your group and work with your group to:

- Find some coordinate pairs that represent solutions to the inequality and some coordinate pairs that do not represent solutions.

- Plot both sets of points. Either use two different colors or two different symbols like X and O.

- Plot enough points until you start to see the region that contains solutions and the region that contains non-solutions. Look for a pattern describing the region where solutions are plotted.

$x \geq y$ $\qquad\qquad\qquad\qquad\qquad$ $-2y \geq -4$

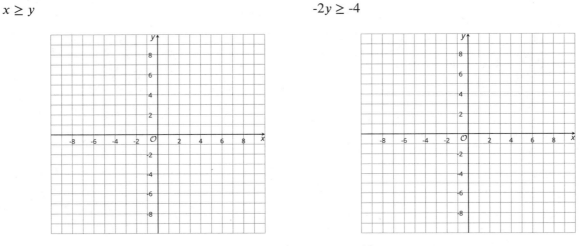

$3x < 0$ $\qquad\qquad\qquad\qquad\qquad$ $x + y > 10$

 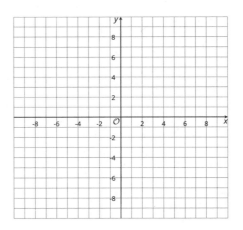

$\qquad\qquad$ Algebra 1 iM KH

21.3: Sketching Solutions to Inequalities

1. Here is a graph that represents solutions to the equation $x - y = 5$.

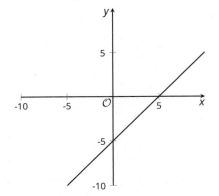

Sketch 4 quick graphs representing the solutions to each of these inequalities:

$x - y < 5$

$x - y \leq 5$

$x - y > 5$

$x - y \geq 5$

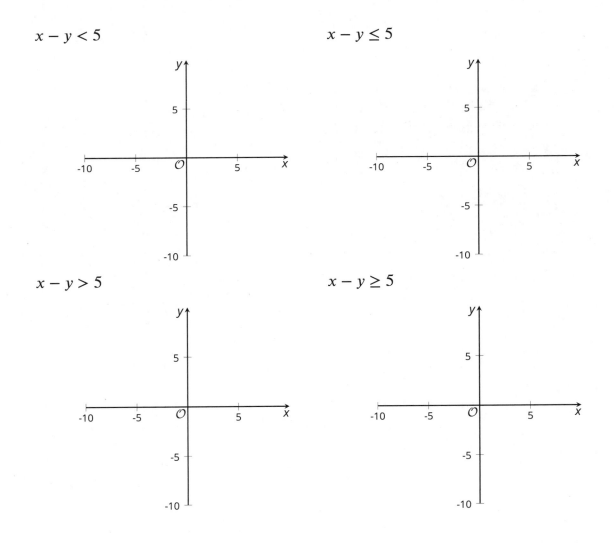

2. For each graph, write an inequality whose solutions are represented by the shaded part of the graph.

A

B

C

D

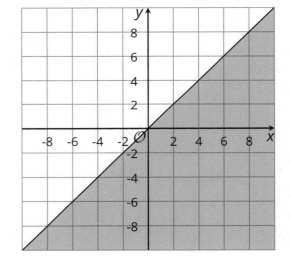

Are you ready for more?

1. The points $(7, 3)$ and $(7, 5)$ are both in the solution region of the inequality $x - 2y < 3$.

   a. Compute $x - 2y$ for both of these points.

   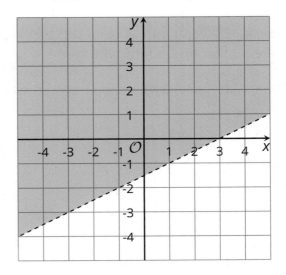

   b. Which point comes closest to satisfying the equation $x - 2y = 3$? That is, for which (x, y) pair is $x - 2y$ closest to 3?

2. The points $(3, 2)$ and $(5, 2)$ are also in the solution region. Which of these points comes closest to satisfying the equation $x - 2y = 3$?

3. Find a point in the solution region that comes even closer to satisfying the equation $x - 2y = 3$. What is the value of $x - 2y$?

4. For the points $(5, 2)$ and $(7, 3)$, $x - 2y = 1$. Find another point in the solution region for which $x - 2y = 1$.

5. Find $x - 2y$ for the point $(5, 3)$. Then find two other points that give the same answer.

Lesson 21 Summary

The equation $x + y = 7$ is an equation in two variables. Its solution is any pair of x and y whose sum is 7. The pairs $x = 0, y = 7$ and $x = 5, y = 2$ are two examples.

We can represent all the solutions to $x + y = 7$ by graphing the equation on a coordinate plane.

The graph is a line. All the points on the line are solutions to $x + y = 7$.

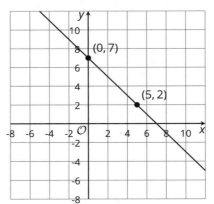

The inequality $x + y \leq 7$ is an inequality in two variables. Its solution is any pair of x and y whose sum is 7 or less than 7.

This means it includes all the pairs that are solutions to the equation $x + y = 7$, but also many other pairs of x and y that add up to a value less than 7. The pairs $x = 4, y = -7$ and $x = -6, y = 0$ are two examples.

On a coordinate plane, the solution to $x + y \leq 7$ includes the line that represents $x + y = 7$. If we plot a few other (x, y) pairs that make the inequality true, such as $(4, -7)$ and $(-6, 0)$, we see that these points fall on one side of the line. (In contrast, (x, y) pairs that make the inequality false fall on the other side of the line.)

We can shade that region on one side of the line to indicate that all points in it are solutions.

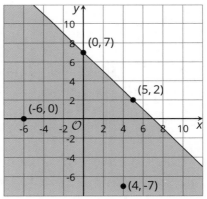

What about the inequality $x + y < 7$?

The solution is any pair of x and y whose sum is less than 7. This means pairs like $x = 0, y = 7$ and $x = 5, y = 2$ are *not* solutions.

Algebra 1   **iM KH**

On a coordinate plane, the solution does not include points on the line that represent $x + y = 7$ (because those points are x and y pairs whose sum is 7).

To exclude points on that boundary line, we can use a dashed line.

All points below that line are (x, y) pairs that make $x + y < 7$ true. The region on that side of the line can be shaded to show that it contains the solutions.

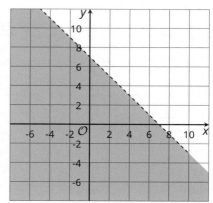

Lesson 21 Practice Problems

1. Here is a graph of the equation $2y - x = 1$.

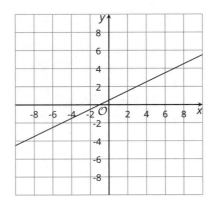

a. Are the points $(0, \frac{1}{2})$ and $(-7, -3)$ solutions to the equation? Explain or show how you know.

b. Check if each of these points is a solution to the inequality $2y - x > 1$:

$$(0, 2) \qquad (8, \tfrac{1}{2}) \qquad (-6, 3) \qquad (-7, -3)$$

c. Shade the region that represents the solution set to the inequality $2y - x > 1$.

d. Are the points on the line included in the solution set? Explain how you know.

2. Select **all** coordinate pairs that are solutions to the inequality $5x + 9y < 45$.

   A. $(0, 0)$

   B. $(5, 0)$

   C. $(9, 0)$

   D. $(0, 5)$

   E. $(0, 9)$

   F. $(5, 9)$

   G. $(-5, -9)$

3. Consider the linear equation $2y - 3x = 5$.

    a. The pair $(-1, 1)$ is a solution to the equation. Find another (x, y) pair that is a solution to the equation.

    b. Are $(-1, 1)$ and $(4, 1)$ solutions to the inequality $2y - 3x < 5$? Explain how you know.

    c. Explain how to use the answers to the previous questions to graph the solution set to the inequality $2y - 3x < 5$.

4. The boundary line on the graph represents the equation $5x + 2y = 6$. Write an inequality that is represented by the graph.

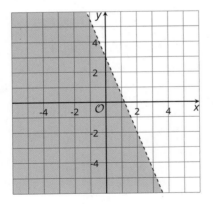

5. Choose the inequality whose solution set is represented by this graph.

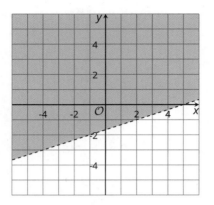

A. $x - 3y < 5$

B. $x - 3y \leq 5$

C. $x - 3y > 5$

D. $x - 3y \geq 5$

6. Solve each system of equations without graphing.

a. $\begin{cases} 4d + 7e = 68 \\ -4d - 6e = -72 \end{cases}$

b. $\begin{cases} \frac{1}{4}x + y = 1 \\ \frac{3}{2}x - y = \frac{4}{3} \end{cases}$

(From Unit 2, Lesson 14.)

Algebra 1

7. Mai and Tyler are selling items to earn money for their elementary school. The school earns w dollars for every wreath sold and p dollars for every potted plant sold. Mai sells 14 wreaths and 3 potted plants and the school earns $70.50. Tyler sells 10 wreaths and 7 potted plants and the school earns $62.50.

   This situation is represented by this system of equations: $\begin{cases} 14w + 3p = 70.50 \\ 10w + 7p = 62.50 \end{cases}$

   Explain why it makes sense in this situation that the solution of this system is also a solution to $4w + (\text{-}4p) = 8.00$.

   (From Unit 2, Lesson 15.)

8. Elena is planning to go camping for the weekend and has already spent $40 on supplies. She goes to the store and buys more supplies.

   Which inequality represents d, the total amount in dollars that Elena spends on supplies?

   A. $d > 40$

   B. $d \geq 40$

   C. $d < 40$

   D. $d \leq 40$

   (From Unit 2, Lesson 18.)

9. Solve this inequality: $\dfrac{x-4}{3} \geq \dfrac{x+3}{2}$

   (From Unit 2, Lesson 19.)

10. Which graph represents the solution to $\dfrac{4x - 8}{3} \leq 2x - 5$?

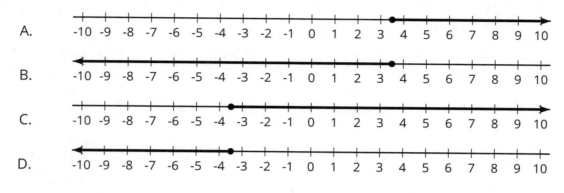

A.

B.

C.

D.

(From Unit 2, Lesson 19.)

11. Solve $-x < 3$. Explain how to find the solution set.

(From Unit 2, Lesson 20.)

Lesson 22: Graphing Linear Inequalities in Two Variables (Part 2)

- Let's write inequalities in two variables and make sense of the solutions by reasoning and by graphing.

22.1: Landscaping Options

A homeowner is making plans to landscape her yard. She plans to hire professionals to install grass sod in some parts of the yard and flower beds in other parts.

Grass sod installation costs $2 per square foot and flower bed installation costs $12 per square foot. Her budget for the project is $3,000.

1. Write an equation that represents the square feet of grass sod, x, and the square feet of flower beds, y, that she could afford if she used her entire budget.

2. On the coordinate plane, sketch a graph that represents your equation. Be prepared to explain your reasoning.

22.2: Rethinking Landscaping

The homeowner is worried about the work needed to maintain a grass lawn and flower beds, so she is now looking at some low-maintenance materials.

She is considering artificial turf, which costs $15 per square foot to install, and gravel, which costs $3 per square foot. She may use a combination of the two materials in different parts of the yard. Her budget is still $3,000.

Here is a graph representing some constraints in this situation.

1. The graph shows a line going through (500, 100).

   a. In this situation, what does the point (500, 100) mean?

   b. Write an equation that the line represents.

   c. What do the solutions to the equation mean?

2. The point (600, 200) is located to the right and above the line.

   a. Does that combination of turf and gravel meet the homeowner's constraints? Explain or show your reasoning.

   b. Choose another point in the same region (to the right and above the line). Check if the combination meet the homeowner's constraints.

3. The point (200, 100) is located to the left and below the line.

    a. Does that combination of turf and gravel meet the homeowner's constraints? Explain or show your reasoning.

    b. Choose another point in the same region (to the left and below the line). Check if the combination meets the homeowner's constraints.

4. Write an inequality that represents the constraints in this situation. Explain what the solutions mean and show the solution region on the graph.

22.3: The Saturday Market

A vendor at the Saturday Market makes $9 profit on each necklace she sells and $5 profit on each bracelet.

1. Find a combination of necklaces and bracelets that she could sell and make:

    a. exactly $100 profit

    b. more than $100 profit

2. Write an equation whose solution is the combination of necklaces and bracelets she could sell and make exactly $100 profit.

3. Write an inequality whose solutions are the combinations of necklaces and bracelets she could sell and make more than $100 profit.

4. Graph the solutions to your inequality.

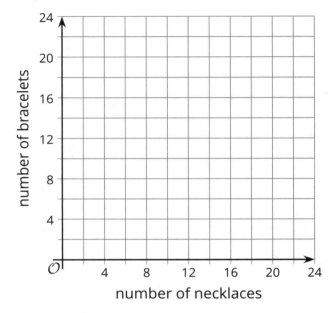

5. Is (3, 18.6) a solution to the inequality? Explain your reasoning.

Are you ready for more?

1. Write an inequality using two variables x and y where the solution would be represented by shading the entire coordinate plane.

2. Write an inequality using two variables x and y where the solution would be represented by not shading any of the coordinate plane.

Algebra 1 iM KH

22.4: Charity Concerts

A popular band is trying to raise at least $20,000 for charity by holding multiple concerts at a park. It plans to sell tickets at $25 each. For each 2-hour concert, the band would need to pay the park $1,250 in fees for security, cleaning, and traffic services.

The band needs to find the combinations of number of tickets sold, t, and number of concerts held, c, that would allow it to reach its fundraising goal.

1. Write an inequality to represent the constraints in this situation.

2. Graph the solutions to the inequality on the coordinate plane.

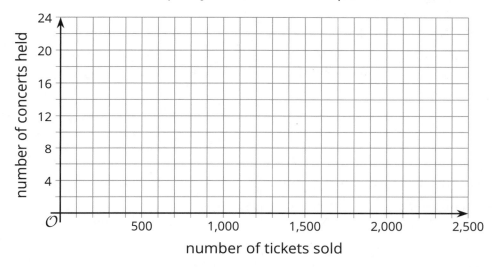

3. Name two possible combinations of number of tickets sold and number of concerts held that would allow the band to meet its goal.

4. Which combination of tickets and concerts would mean *more* money for charity:

    a. 1,300 tickets and 10 concerts, or 1,300 tickets and 5 concerts?

    b. 1,600 tickets and 16 concerts, or 1,200 tickets and 9 concerts?

    c. 2,000 tickets and 4 concerts, or 2,500 tickets and 10 concerts?

Lesson 22 Summary

Inequalities in two variables can represent constraints in real-life situations. Graphing their solutions can enable us to solve problems.

Suppose a café is purchasing coffee and tea from a supplier and can spend up to $1,000. Coffee beans cost $12 per kilogram and tea leaves costs $8 per kilogram.

Buying c pounds of coffee beans and t pounds of tea leaves will therefore cost $12c + 8t$. To represent the budget constraints, we can write: $12c + 8t \leq 1,000$.

The solution to this inequality is any pair of c and t that makes the inequality true. In this situation, it is any combination of the pounds of coffee and tea that the café can order without going over the $1,000 budget.

We can try different pairs of c and t to see what combinations satisfy the constraint, but it would be difficult to capture all the possible combinations this way. Instead, we can graph a related equation, $12c + 8t = 1,000$, and then find out which region represents all possible solutions.

Here is the graph of that equation.

To determine the solution region, let's take one point on the line and one point on each side of the line, and see if the pairs of values produce true statements.

A point on the line: $(30, 80)$

$$12(30) + 8(80) \leq 1,000$$
$$360 + 640 \leq 1,000$$
$$1,000 \leq 1,000$$

This is true.

A point below the line: $(20, 40)$

$$12(20) + 8(40) \leq 1,000$$
$$240 + 320 \leq 1,000$$
$$560 \leq 1,000$$

This is true.

A point above the line: $(70, 100)$

$$12(70) + 8(100) \leq 1,000$$
$$840 + 800 \leq 1,000$$
$$1,640 \leq 1,000$$

This is false.

The points on the line and in the region below the line are solutions to the inequality. Let's shade the solution region.

It is easy to read solutions from the graph. For example, without any computation, we can tell that $(50, 20)$ is a solution because it falls in the shaded region. If the café orders 50 kilograms of coffee and 20 kilograms of tea, the cost will be less than $1,000.

Lesson 22 Practice Problems

1. To qualify for a loan from a bank, the total in someone's checking and savings accounts together must be $500 or more.

   a. Which of these inequalities best represents this situation?

   ■ $x + y < 500$

   ■ $x + y \leq 500$

   ■ $x + y > 500$

   ■ $x + y \geq 500$

   b. Complete the graph so that it represents solutions to an inequality representing this situation.

   (Be clear about whether you want to use a solid or dashed line.)

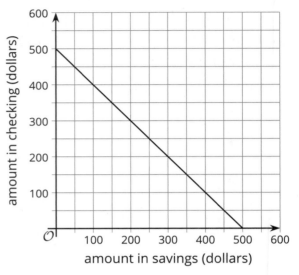

2. The soccer team is selling bags of popcorn for $3 each and cups of lemonade for $2 each. To make a profit, they must collect a total of more than $120.

   a. Write an inequality to represent the number of bags of popcorn sold, p, and the number of cups of lemonade sold, c, in order to make a profit.

   b. Graph the solution set to the inequality on the coordinate plane.

   c. Explain how we could check if the boundary is included or excluded from the solution region.

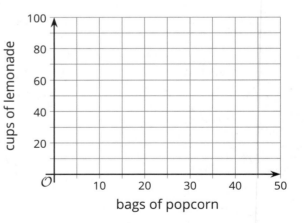

3. Tickets to the aquarium are $11 for adults and $6 for children. An after-school program has a budget of $200 for a trip to the aquarium.

If the boundary line in each graph represents the equation $11x + 6y = 200$, which graph represents the cost constraint in this situation?

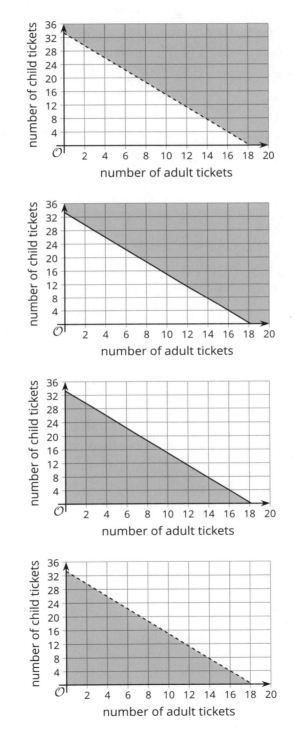

A.

B.

C.

D.

4. Tyler filled a small jar with quarters and dimes and donated it to his school's charity club. The club member receiving the jar asked, "Do you happen to know how much is in the jar?" Tyler said, "I know it's at least $8.50, but I don't know the exact amount."

a. Write an inequality to represent the relationship between the number of dimes, d, the number of quarters, q, and the dollar amount of the money in the jar.

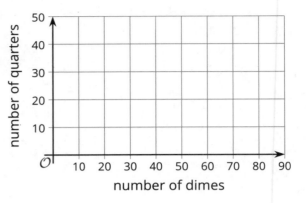

b. Graph the solution set to the inequality and explain what a solution means in this situation.

c. Suppose Tyler knew there are 25 dimes in the jar. Write an inequality that represents how many quarters could be in the jar.

5. Andre is solving the inequality $14x + 3 \leq 8x + 3$. He first solves a related equation.

$$14x + 3 = 8x + 3$$
$$14x = 8x$$
$$8 = 14$$

This seems strange to Andre. He thinks he probably made a mistake. What was his mistake?

(From Unit 2, Lesson 20.)

6. Kiran says, "I bought 2.5 pounds of red and yellow lentils. Both were $1.80 per pound. I spent a total of $4.05."

   a. Write a system of equations to describe the relationships between the quantities in Kiran's statement. Be sure to specify what each variable represents.

   b. Elena says, "That can't be right." Explain how Elena can tell that something is wrong with Kiran's statement.

   c. Kiran says, "Oops, I meant to say I bought 2.25 pounds of lentils." Revise your system of equations to reflect this correction.

   d. Is it possible to tell for sure how many pounds of each kind of lentil Kiran might have bought? Explain your reasoning.

(From Unit 2, Lesson 17.)

7. Here is an inequality: $-7 - (3x + 2) < -8(x + 1)$

Select **all** the values of x that are solutions to the inequality.

A. $x = -0.2$

B. $x = -0.1$

C. $x = 0$

D. $x = 0.1$

E. $x = 0.2$

F. $x = 0.3$

(From Unit 2, Lesson 19.)

8. Here is a graph of the equation $6x + 2y = -8$.

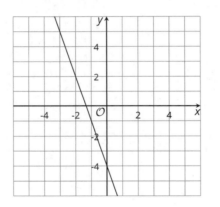

a. Are the points $(1.5, -4)$ and $(0, -4)$ solutions to the equation? Explain or show how you know.

b. Check if each of these points is a solution to the inequality $6x + 2y \leq -8$:

$(-2, 2)$ $(4, -2)$ $(0, 0)$ $(-4, -4)$

c. Shade the solutions to the inequality.

d. Are the points on the line included in the solution region? Explain how you know.

(From Unit 2, Lesson 21.)

Lesson 23: Solving Problems with Inequalities in Two Variables

- Let's practice writing, interpreting, and graphing solutions to inequalities in two variables.

23.1: Graphing Inequalities with Technology

Use graphing technology to graph the solution region of each inequality and sketch each graph. Adjust the graphing window as needed to show meaningful information.

$y > x$ $\qquad\qquad$ $y \geq x$ $\qquad\qquad$ $y < \text{-}8$

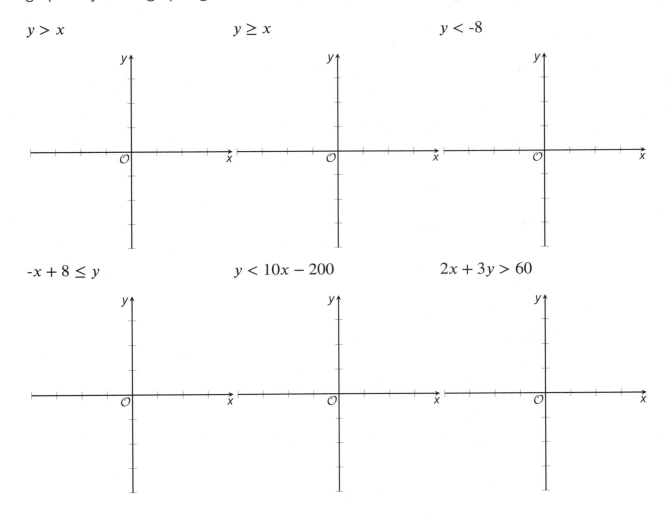

$\text{-}x + 8 \leq y$ $\qquad\qquad$ $y < 10x - 200$ $\qquad\qquad$ $2x + 3y > 60$

23.2: Solving Problems with Inequalities in Two Variables

Here are three situations. There are two questions about each situation. For each question that you work on:

a. Write an inequality to describe the constraints. Specify what each variable represents.

b. Use graphing technology to graph the inequality. Sketch the solution region on the coordinate plane and label the axes.

c. Name one solution to the inequality and explain what it represents in that situation.

d. Answer the question about the situation.

Bank Accounts

1. A customer opens a checking account and a savings account at a bank. They will deposit a maximum of $600, some in the checking account and some in the savings account. (They might not deposit all of it and keep some of the money as cash.)

   If the customer deposits $200 in their checking account, what can you say about the amount they deposit in their savings account?

2. The bank requires a minimum balance of $50 in the savings account. It does not matter how much money is kept in the checking account.

   If the customer deposits no money in the checking account but is able to maintain both accounts without penalty, what can you say about the amount deposited in the savings account?

Concert Tickets

1. Two kinds of tickets to an outdoor concert were sold: lawn tickets and seat tickets. Fewer than 400 tickets in total were sold.

   If you know that exactly 100 lawn tickets were sold, what can you say about the number of seat tickets?

2. Lawn tickets cost $30 each and seat tickets cost $50 each. The organizers want to make at least $14,000 from ticket sales.

   If you know that exactly 200 seat tickets were sold, what can you say about the number of lawn tickets?

Advertising Packages

1. An advertising agency offers two packages for small businesses who need advertising services. A basic package includes only design services. A premium package includes design and promotion. The agency's goal is to sell at least 60 packages in total.

   If the agency sells exactly 45 basic packages, what can you say about the number of premium packages it needs to sell to meet its goal?

2. The basic advertising package has a value of $1,000 and the premium package has a value of $2,500. The goal of the agency is to sell more than $60,000 worth of small-business advertising packages.

   If you know that exactly 10 premium packages were sold, what can you say about the number of basic packages the agency needs to sell to meet its goal?

Are you ready for more?

This activity will require a partner.

1. Without letting your partner see it, write an equation of a line so that both the x-intercept and the y-intercept are each between -3 and 3. Graph your equation on one of the coordinate systems.

Your Inequality   **Your Partner's Inequality**

  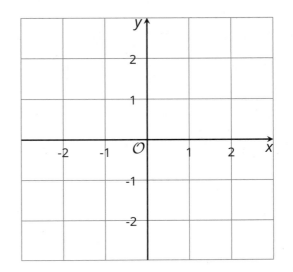

2. Still without letting your partner see it, write an inequality for which your equation is the related equation. In other words, your line should be the boundary between solutions and non-solutions. Shade the solutions on your graph.

3. Take turns stating coordinates of points. Your partner will tell you whether your guess is a solution to their inequality. After each partner has stated a point, each may guess what the other's inequality is. If neither guesses correctly, play continues. Use the other coordinate system to keep track of your guesses.

23.3: Card Sort: Representations of Inequalities

Your teacher will give you a set of cards. Take turns with your partner to match a group of 4 cards that contain: a situation, an inequality that represents it, a graph that represents the solution region, and a solution written as a coordinate pair.

For each match that you find, explain to your partner how you know it's a match.

For each match that your partner finds, listen carefully to their explanation. If you disagree, discuss your thinking and work to reach an agreement.

Record your matches.

Group 1

- situation: perimeter of a rectangle

- inequality:

- a solution:

- sketch of graph:

Group 2

- situation: jar of coins

- inequality:

- a solution:

- sketch of graph:

Group 3

- situation: honey and jam

- inequality:

- a solution:

- sketch of graph:

Group 4

- situation: a school trip

- inequality:

- a solution:

- sketch of graph:

Lesson 23 Summary

Suppose we want to find the solution to $x - y > 5$. We can start by graphing the related equation $x - y = 5$.

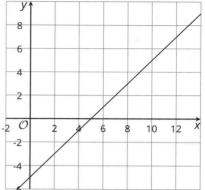

When identifying the solution region, it is important *not* to assume that the solution will be above the line because of a ">" symbol or below the line because of a "<" symbol.

Instead, test the points on the line and on either side of the line and see if they are solutions.

For $x - y > 5$, points on the line and above the line are *not* solutions to the inequality because the (x, y) pairs make the inequality false. Points that are below the lines are solutions, so we can shade that lower region.

Graphing technology can help us graph the solution to an inequality in two variables.

Many graphing tools allow us to enter inequalities such as $x - y > 5$ and will show the solution region, as shown here.

Some tools, however, may require the inequalities to be in slope-intercept form or another form before displaying the solution region. Be sure to learn how to use the graphing technology available in your classroom.

Although graphing using technology is efficient, we still need to analyze the graph with care. Here are some things to consider:

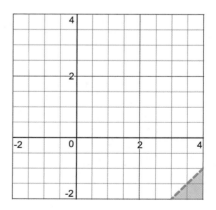

- The graphing window. If the graphing window is too small, we may not be able to really see the solution region or the boundary line, as shown here.

- The meaning of solution points in the situation. For example, if x and y represent the lengths of two sides of a rectangle, then only positive values of x and y (or points in the first quadrant) make sense in the situation.

Lesson 23 Practice Problems

1. This year, students in the 9th grade are collecting dimes and quarters for a school fundraiser. They are trying to collect more money than the students who were in the 9th grade last year. The students in 9th grade last year collected $143.88.

   Using d to represent the number of dimes collected and q to represent the number of quarters, which statement best represents this situation?

   A. $0.25d + 0.1q \geq 143.88$

   B. $0.25q + 0.1d \geq 143.88$

   C. $0.25d + 0.1q > 143.88$

   D. $0.25q + 0.1d > 143.88$

2. A farmer is creating a budget for planting soybeans and wheat. Planting soybeans costs $200 per acre and planting wheat costs $500 per acre. He wants to spend no more than $100,000 planting soybeans and wheat.

   a. Write an inequality to describe the constraints. Specify what each variable represents.

   b. Name one solution to the inequality and explain what it represents in that situation.

3. Elena is ordering dried chili peppers and corn husks for her cooking class. Chili peppers cost $16.95 per pound and corn husks cost $6.49 per pound.

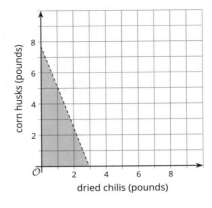

Elena spends less than $50 on d pounds of dried chili peppers and h pounds of corn husks.

Here is a graph that represents this situation.

    a. Write an inequality that represents this situation.

    b. Can Elena purchase 2 pounds of dried chili peppers and 4 pounds of corn husks and spend less than $50? Explain your reasoning.

    c. Can Elena purchase 1.5 pounds of dried chili peppers and 3 pounds of corn husks and spend less than $50? Explain your reasoning.

4. Which inequality is represented by the graph?

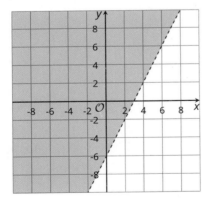

    A. $4x - 2y > 12$

    B. $4x - 2y < 12$

    C. $4x + 2y > 12$

    D. $4x + 2y < 12$

5. Here are some statistics for the number of minutes it took each of 9 members of the track team to run 1 mile.

   When a tenth time is added to the list, the standard deviation increases to 1.5. Is the tenth time likely an outlier? Explain your reasoning.

   ○ mean: 7.3

   ○ median: 7.1

   ○ standard deviation: 1.1

   ○ Q1: 6.8

   ○ Q3: 7.4

(From Unit 1, Lesson 14.)

6. Elena is solving this system of equations: $\begin{cases} 10x - 6y = 16 \\ 5x - 3y = 8 \end{cases}$

   She multiplies the second equation by 2, then subtracts the resulting equation from the first. To her surprise, she gets the equation $0 = 0$.

   What is special about this system of equations? Why does she get this result and what does it mean about the solutions? (If you are not sure, try graphing them.)

(From Unit 2, Lesson 17.)

7. Jada has a sleeping bag that is rated for 30° F. This means that if the temperature outside is at least 30° F, Jada will be able to stay warm in her sleeping bag.

   a. Write an inequality that represents the outdoor temperature at which Jada will be able to stay warm in her sleeping bag.

   b. Write an inequality that represents the outdoor temperature at which a thicker or warmer sleeping bag would be needed to keep Jada warm.

(From Unit 2, Lesson 18.)

8. What is the solution set to this inequality: $6x - 20 > 3(2 - x) + 6x - 2$?

(From Unit 2, Lesson 19.)

9. Here is a graph of the equation $2x - 3y = 15$.

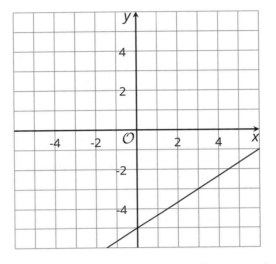

a. Are the points (1.5, -4) and (4, -4) solutions to the equation? Explain or show how you know.

b. Check if each of these points is a solution to the inequality $2x - 3y < 15$:

(0, -5)   (4, -2)   (2, -4)   (5, -1)

c. Shade the solutions to the inequality .

d. Are the points on the line included in the solution region? Explain how you know.

(From Unit 2, Lesson 21.)

Algebra 1

10. A store sells notepads in packages of 24 and packages of 6. The organizers of a conference needs to prepare at least 200 notepads for the event.

   a. Would they have enough notepads if they bought these quantities?

      i. Seven packages of 24 and one package of 6

      ii. Five packages of 24 and fifteen packages of 6 ˅

   b. Write an inequality to represent the relationship between the number of large and small packages of notepads and the number of notepads needed for the event.

   c. Use graphing technology to graph the solution set to the inequality. Then, use the graph to name two other possible combinations of large and small packages of notepads that will meet the number of notepads needed for the event.

   (From Unit 2, Lesson 22.)

Lesson 24: Solutions to Systems of Linear Inequalities in Two Variables

- Let's look at situations where two constraints (that can be expressed by inequalities) must be met simultaneously.

24.1: A Silly Riddle

Here is a riddle: "I am thinking of two numbers that add up to 5.678. The difference between them is 9.876. What are the two numbers?"

1. Name any pair of numbers whose sum is 5.678.

$$X + y = 5.678$$

2. Name any pair of numbers whose difference is 9.876.

$$X - y = 9.876$$

3. The riddle can be represented with two equations. Write the equations.

$$(7.777, -2.099)$$

4. Solve the riddle. Explain or show your reasoning.

24.2: A Quilting Project

To make a quilt, a quilter is buying fabric in two colors, light and dark. He needs at least 9.5 yards of fabric in total.

The light color costs $9 a yard. The dark color costs $13 a yard. The quilter can spend up to $110 on fabric.

Here are two graphs that represent the two constraints.

A   B

dark fabric (yards) / light fabric (yards)

1. Write an inequality to represent the length constraint. Let x represent the yards of light fabric and y represent the yards of dark fabric.

$x + y \geq 9.5$ $9x + 13y \leq 110$ $x = 0$ $y = 13y$

2. Select **all** the pairs that satisfy the length constraint.

   $(5, 5)$ $(2.5, 4.5)$ $(7.5, 3.5)$ $(12, 10)$

3. Write an inequality to represent the cost constraint.

4. Select **all** the pairs that satisfy the cost constraint.

   $(1, 1)$ $(4, 5)$ $(8, 3)$ $(10, 1)$

5. Explain why $(2, 2)$ satisfies the cost constraint, but not the length constraint.

6. Find at least one pair of numbers that satisfies *both* constraints. Be prepared to explain how you know.

7. What does the pair of numbers represent in this situation?

Algebra 1 iM KH

24.3: Remember These Situations?

Here are some situations you have seen before. Answer the questions for one situation.

Bank Accounts

- A customer opens a checking account and a savings account at a bank. They will deposit a maximum of $600, some in the checking account and some in the savings account. (They might not deposit all of it and keep some of the money as cash.)

- The bank requires a minimum balance of $50 in the savings account. It does not matter how much money is kept in the checking account.

Concert Tickets

- Two kinds of tickets to an outdoor concert were sold: lawn tickets and seat tickets. Fewer than 400 tickets in total were sold.

- Lawn tickets cost $30 each and seat tickets cost $50 each. The organizers want to make at least $14,000 from ticket sales.

Advertising Packages

- An advertising agency offers two packages for small businesses who need advertising services. A basic package includes only design services. A premium package includes design and promotion. The agency's goal is to sell at least 60 packages in total.

- The basic advertising package has a value of $1,000 and the premium package has a value of $2,500. The goal of the agency is to sell more than $60,000 worth of small-business advertising packages.

1. Write a **system of inequalities** to represent the constraints. Specify what each variable represents.

2. Use technology to graph the inequalities and sketch the solution regions. Include labels and scales for the axes.

3. Identify **a solution to the system**. Explain what the numbers mean in the situation.

24.4: Scavenger Hunt

Members of a high school math club are doing a scavenger hunt. Three items are hidden in the park, which is a rectangle that measures 50 meters by 20 meters.

- The clues are written as systems of inequalities. One system has no solutions.

- The locations of the items can be narrowed down by solving the systems. A coordinate plane can be used to describe the solutions.

Can you find the hidden items? Sketch a graph to show where each item could be hidden.

Clue 1: $y > 14$
            $x < 10$

Clue 2: $x + y < 20$
            $x > 6$

Clue 3: $y < -2x + 20$
            $y < -2x + 10$

Clue 4: $y \geq x + 10$
            $x > y$ no solution

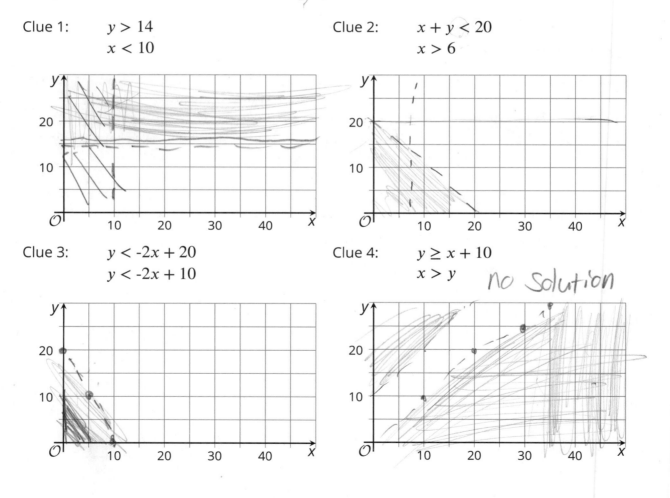

Are you ready for more?

Two non-negative numbers x and y satisfy $x + y \leq 1$.

1. Find a second inequality, also using x and y values greater than or equal to zero, to make a system of inequalities with exactly one solution.

2. Find as many ways to answer this question as you can.

Lesson 24 Summary

In this lesson, we used two linear inequalities in two variables to represent the constraints in a situation. Each pair of inequalities forms a **system of inequalities**.

A **solution to the system** is any (x, y) pair that makes both inequalities true, or any pair of values that simultaneously meet both constraints in the situation. The solution to the system is often best represented by a region on a graph.

Suppose there are two numbers, x and y, and there are two things we know about them:

- The value of one number is more than double the value of the other.

- The sum of the two numbers is less than 10.

We can represent these constraints with a system of inequalities.

$$\begin{cases} y > 2x \\ x + y < 10 \end{cases}$$

There are many possible pairs of numbers that meet the first constraint, for example: 1 and 3, or 4 and 9.

The same can be said about the second constraint, for example: 1 and 3, or 2.4 and 7.5.

The pair $x = 1$ and $y = 3$ meets both constraints, so it is a solution to the system.

The pair $x = 4$ and $y = 9$ meets the first constraint but not the second ($9 > 2(4)$ is a true statement, but $4 + 9 < 10$ is not true.)

Remember that graphing is a great way to show all the possible solutions to an inequality, so let's graph the solution region for each inequality.

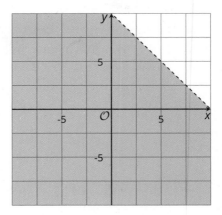

Because we are looking for a pair of numbers that meet both constraints or make both inequalities true at the same time, we want to find points that are in the solution regions of both graphs.

To do that, we can graph both inequalities on the same coordinate plane.

The solution set to the system of inequalities is represented by the region where the two graphs overlap.

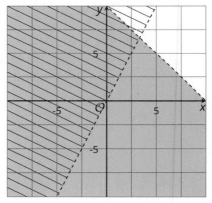

Glossary

- solutions to a system of inequalities
- system of inequalities

Lesson 24 Practice Problems

1. Two inequalities are graphed on the same coordinate plane.

   Which region represents the solution to the system of the two inequalities?

   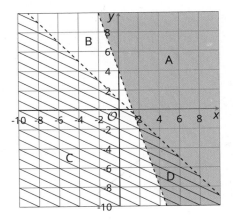

2. Select **all** the pairs of x and y that are solutions to the system of inequalities:

$$\begin{cases} y \leq -2x + 6 \\ x - y < 6 \end{cases}$$

   A. $x = 0, y = 0$

   B. $x = -5, y = -15$

   C. $x = 4, y = -2$

   D. $x = 3, y = 0$

   E. $x = 10, y = 0$

3. Jada has $200 to spend on flowers for a school celebration. She decides that the only flowers that she wants to buy are roses and carnations. Roses cost $1.45 each and carnations cost $0.65 each. Jada buys enough roses so that each of the 75 people attending the event can take home at least one rose.

   a. Write an inequality to represent the constraint that every person takes home at least one rose.

   b. Write an inequality to represent the cost constraint.

4. Here are the graphs of the equations $3x + y = 9$ and $3x - y = 9$ on the same coordinate plane.

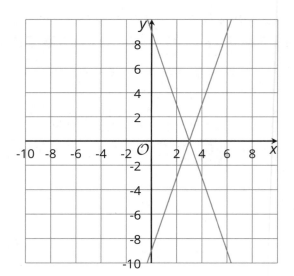

a. Label each graph with the equation it represents.

b. Identify the region that represents the solution set to $3x + y < 9$. Is the boundary line a part of the solution? Use a colored pencil or cross-hatching to shade the region.

c. Identify the region that represents the solution set to $3x - y < 9$. Is the boundary line a part of the solution? Use a different colored pencil or cross-hatching to shade the region.

d. Identify a point that is a solution to both $3x + y < 9$ and $3x - y < 9$.

5. Which coordinate pair is a solution to the inequality $4x - 2y < 22$?

   A. $(4, -3)$

   B. $(4, 3)$

   C. $(8, -3)$

   D. $(8, 3)$

   (From Unit 2, Lesson 21.)

6. Consider the linear equation $9x - 3y = 12$.

 a. The pair $(3, 5)$ is a solution to the equation. Find another pair (x, y) that is a solution to the equation.

 b. Are $(3, 5)$ and $(2, -10)$ solutions to the inequality $9x - 3y \leq 12$? Explain how you know.

(From Unit 2, Lesson 21.)

7. Elena is considering buying bracelets and necklaces as gifts for her friends. Bracelets cost \$3, and necklaces cost \$5. She can spend no more than \$30 on the gifts.

 a. Write an inequality to represent the number of bracelets, b, and the number of necklaces n, she could buy while sticking to her budget.

 b. Graph the solutions to the inequality on the coordinate plane.

 c. Explain how we could check if the boundary is included or excluded from the solution set.

(From Unit 2, Lesson 22.)

8. In physical education class, Mai takes 10 free throws and 10 jump shots. She earns 1 point for each free throw she makes and 2 points for each jump shot she makes. The greatest number of points that she can earn is 30.

   a. Write an inequality to describe the constraints. Specify what each variable represents.

   b. Name one solution to the inequality and explain what it represents in that situation.

(From Unit 2, Lesson 23.)

9. A rectangle with a width of w and a length of l has a perimeter greater than 100.

   Here is a graph that represents this situation.

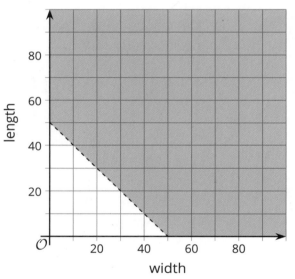

   a. Write an inequality that represents this situation.

   b. Can the rectangle have width of 45 and a length of 10? Explain your reasoning.

   c. Can the rectangle have a width of 30 and a length of 20? Explain your reasoning.

(From Unit 2, Lesson 23.)

Algebra 1 iM **KH**

Lesson 25: Solving Problems with Systems of Linear Inequalities in Two Variables

- Let's use systems of inequalities to solve some problems.

25.1: Which One Doesn't Belong: Graphs of Solutions

Which one doesn't belong?

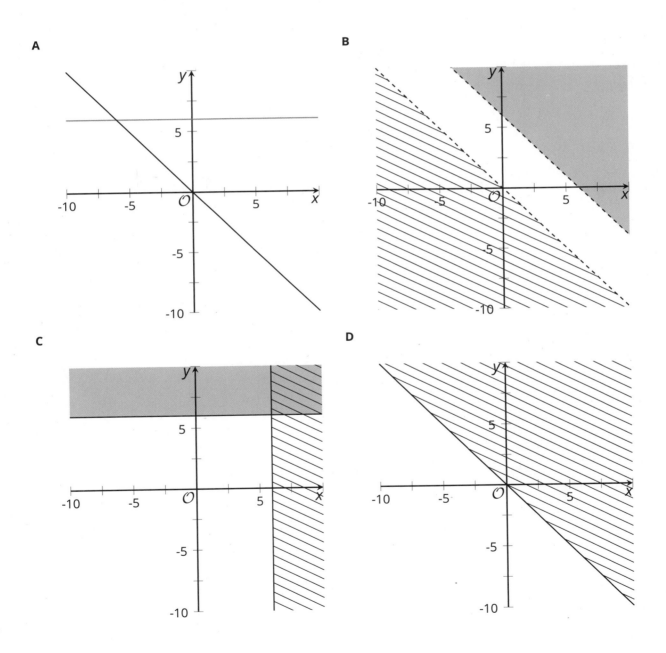

A

B

C

D

25.2: Focusing on the Details

Here are the graphs of the inequalities in this system:

$$\begin{cases} x < y \\ y \geq -2x - 6 \end{cases}$$

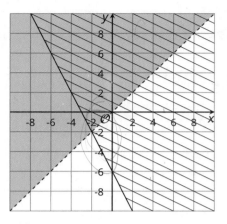

Decide whether each point is a solution to the system. Be prepared to explain how you know.

1. $(3, -5)$

2. $(0, 5)$

3. $(-6, 6)$

4. $(3, 3)$

5. $(-2, -2)$

Are you ready for more?

Find a system of inequalities with this triangle as its set of solutions.

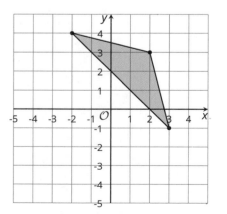

Algebra 1 iM KH

25.3: Info Gap: Terms of A Team

Your teacher will give you either a problem card or a data card. Do not show or read your card to your partner.

If your teacher gives you the data card:

1. Silently read the information on your card.
2. Ask your partner "What specific information do you need?" and wait for your partner to ask for information. Only give information that is on your card. (Do not figure out anything for your partner!)
3. Before telling your partner the information, ask "Why do you need to know (that piece of information)?"
4. Read the problem card, and solve the problem independently.
5. Share the data card, and discuss your reasoning.

If your teacher gives you the problem card:

1. Silently read your card and think about what information you need to answer the question.
2. Ask your partner for the specific information that you need.
3. Explain to your partner how you are using the information to solve the problem.
4. When you have enough information, share the problem card with your partner, and solve the problem independently.
5. Read the data card, and discuss your reasoning.

Pause here so your teacher can review your work. Ask your teacher for a new set of cards and repeat the activity, trading roles with your partner.

The blank coordinate planes are provided here in case they are useful.

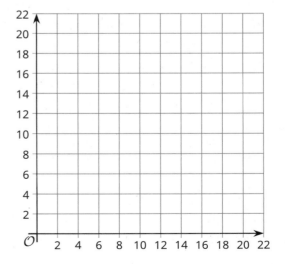

Lesson 25 Summary

A family has at most $25 to spend on activities at Fun Zone. It costs $10 an hour to use the trampolines and $5 an hour to use the pool. The family can stay less than 4 hours.

What are some combinations of trampoline time and pool time that the family could choose given their constraints?

We could find some combinations by trial and error, but writing a system of inequalities and graphing the solution would allow us to see all the possible combinations.

Let t represent the time, in hours, on the trampolines and p represent the time, in hours, in the pool.

The constraints can be represented with the system of inequalities:

$$\begin{cases} 10t + 5p \leq 25 \\ t + p < 4 \end{cases}$$

Here are graphs of the inequalities in the system.

The solution set to the system is represented by the region where shaded parts of the two graphs overlap. Any point in that region is a pair of times that meet both the time and budget constraints.

The graphs give us a complete picture of the possible solutions.

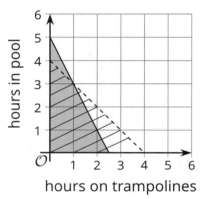

- Can the family spend 1 hour on the trampolines and 3 hours in the pool?

  No. We can reason that it is because those times add up to 4 hours, and the family wants to spend *less than* 4 hours. But we can also see that the point $(1, 3)$ lies on the dashed line of one graph, so it is not a solution.

- Can the family spend 2 hours on the trampolines and 1.5 hours in the pool?

  No. We know that these two times add up to less than 4 hours, but to find out the cost, we need to calculate $10(2) + 5(1.5)$, which is 27.5 and is more than the budget.

  It may be easier to know that this combination is not an option by noticing that the point $(2, 1.5)$ is in the region with line shading, but not in the region with solid shading. This means it meets one constraint but not the other.

Algebra 1 iM KH

Lesson 25 Practice Problems

1. Jada has p pennies and n nickels that add up to more than 40 cents. She has fewer than 20 coins altogether.

    a. Write a system of inequalities that represents how many pennies and nickels that Jada could have.

    b. Is it possible that Jada has each of the following combinations of coins? If so, explain or show how you know. If not, state which constraint—the amount of money or the number of coins—it does not meet.

        i. 15 pennies and 5 nickels

        ii. 16 pennies and 2 nickels

        iii. 10 pennies and 8 nickels

2. A triathlon athlete swims at an average rate 2.4 miles per hour, and bikes at an average rate of 16.1 miles per hour. At the end of one training session, she has swum and biked more than 20 miles in total.

The inequality $2.4s + 16.1b > 20$ and this graph represent the relationship between the hours of swimming, s, the hours of biking, h, and the total distance the athlete could have traveled in miles.

Mai said, "I'm not sure the graph is right. For example, the point $(10, 3)$ is in the shaded region, but it's not realistic for an athlete to swim for 10 hours and bike for 3 hours in a training session! I think triathlon athletes generally train for no more than 2 hours a day."

   a. Write an inequality to represent Mai's last statement.

   b. Graph the solution set to your inequality.

   c. Determine a possible combination of swimming and biking times that meet both the distance and the time constraints in this situation.

3. Elena is considering buying bracelets and necklaces as gifts for her friends. Bracelets cost $3, and necklaces cost $5. She can spend no more than $30 on the gifts. Elena needs at least 7 gift items.

This graph represents the inequality $3b + 5n \leq 30$, which describes the cost constraint in this situation.

Let b represent the number of bracelets and n the number of necklaces.

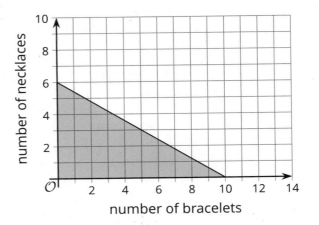

a. Write an inequality that represents the number of gift items that Elena needs.

b. On the same coordinate plane, graph the solution set to the inequality you wrote.

c. Use the graphs to find at least two possible combinations of bracelets and necklaces Elena could buy.

d. Explain how the graphs show that the combination of 2 bracelets and 5 necklaces meet one constraint in the situation but not the other constraint.

4. A gardener is buying some topsoil and compost to fill his garden. His budget is $70. Topsoil costs $1.89 per cubic foot, and compost costs $4.59 per cubic foot.

Select **all** statements or representations that correctly describe the gardener's constraints in this situation. Let t represent the cubic feet of topsoil and c the cubic feet of compost.

A. The combination of 7.5 cubic feet of topsoil and 12 cubic feet of compost is within the gardener's budget.

B. If the line represents the equation $1.89t + 4.59c = 70$, this graph represents the solutions to the gardener's budget constraint.

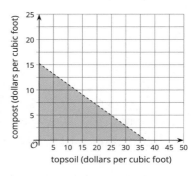

C. $1.89t + 4.59c \geq 70$

D. The combination of 5 cubic feet of topsoil and 20 cubic feet of compost is within the gardener's budget.

E. $1.89t + 4.59c \leq 70$

F. If the line represents the equation $1.89t + 4.59c = 70$, this graph represents the solutions to the gardener's budget constraint.

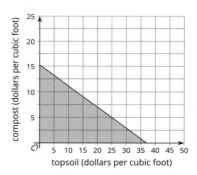

(From Unit 2, Lesson 22.)

5. Priya writes the equation $y = -\frac{1}{2}x - 7$. Write an equation that has:

    a. exactly one solution in common with Priya's equation

    b. no solutions in common with Priya's equation

    c. infinitely many solutions in common with Priya's equation, but looks different than hers

(From Unit 2, Lesson 17.)

6. Two inequalities are graphed on the same coordinate plane.

Which region represents the solution to the system of the two inequalities?

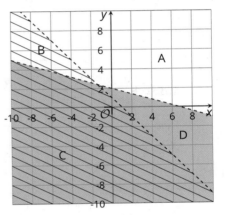

(From Unit 2, Lesson 24.)

7. Here is a riddle:

    ○ The sum of two numbers is less than 10.

    ○ If we subtract the second number from the first, the difference is greater than 3.

Write a system of inequalities that represents this situation. Let f represent the first number and s represent the second number.

(From Unit 2, Lesson 24.)

Lesson 26: Modeling with Systems of Inequalities in Two Variables

- Let's create mathematical models using systems of inequalities.

26.1: A Solution to Which Inequalities?

Is the ordered pair $(5.43, 0)$ a solution to all, some, or none of these inequalities? Be prepared to explain your reasoning.

$$x > 0 \checkmark \qquad y > 0 \quad X \qquad x \geq 0 \checkmark \qquad y \geq 0 \checkmark$$

26.2: Custom Trail Mix

Here is the nutrition information for some trail mix ingredients:

	calories per gram (kcal)	protein per gram (g)	sugar per gram (g)	fat per gram (g)	fiber per gram (g)
peanuts	5.36	0.21	0.04	0.46	0.07
almonds	5.71	0.18	0.21	0.46	0.07
raisins	3.00	0.03	0.60	0.00	0.05
chocolate pieces	4.76	0.05	0.67	0.19	0.02
shredded coconut	6.67	0.07	0.07	0.67	0.13
sunflower seeds	5.50	0.20	0.03	0.47	0.10
dried cherries	3.25	0.03	0.68	0.00	0.03
walnuts	6.43	0.14	0.04	0.61	0.07

Tyler and Jada each designed their own custom trail mix using two of these ingredients. They wrote inequalities and created graphs to represent their constraints.

Tyler

- $x + y > 50$
- $4.76x + 6.67y \leq 400$
- $0.67x + 0.07y < 30$
- $x > 0$ y axis
- $y > 0$ x axis

Jada

- $w + z > 50$
- $0.14w + 0.03z > 4$
- $0.61w + 0z \leq 15$
- $w > 0$
- $z > 0$

Use the inequalities and graphs to answer these questions about each student's trail mix. Be prepared to explain your reasoning.

1. Which two ingredients did they choose?

2. What do their variables represent?

3. What does each constraint mean?

4. Which graph represents which constraint?

5. Name one possible combination of ingredients for their trail mix.

26.3: Design Your Own Trail Mix

It's time to design your own trail mix!

1. Choose two ingredients that you like to eat. (You can choose from the ingredients in the previous activity, or you can look up nutrition information for other ingredients.)

   chocolat covered Pretzels and almonds

2. Think about the constraints for your trail mix. What do you want to be true about its calories, protein, sugar, fat, or fiber?

   total Calories is less than 250

   $c + a < 250$

3. Write inequalities to represent your constraints. Then, graph the inequalities.

   $C + a < 250$

   $24c + 7a < 250$

4. Is it possible to make trail mix that meets all your constraints using your ingredients? If not, make changes to your constraints or your ingredients and record them here.

5. Write a possible combination of ingredients for your trail mix.

Pause here so your teacher can review your work and give further instructions for displaying your work.

Lesson 26 Practice Problems

1. The organizers of a conference needs to prepare at least 200 notepads for the event and have a budget of $160 for the notepads. A store sells notepads in packages of 24 and packages of 6.

   This system of inequalities represent these constraints: $\begin{cases} 24x + 6y \geq 200 \\ 16x + 5.40y \leq 160 \end{cases}$

   a. Explain what the second inequality in the system tells us about the situation.

   b. Here are incomplete graphs of the inequalities in the system, showing only the boundary lines of the solution regions.

      Which graph represents the boundary line of the second inequality?

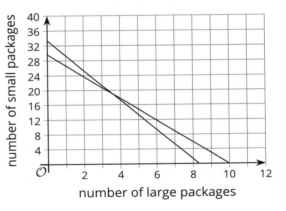

   c. Complete the graphs to show the solution set to the system of inequalities.

   d. Find a possible combination of large and small packages of notepads the organizer could order.

   (From Unit 2, Lesson 25.)

2. A certain stylist charges $15 for a haircut and $30 for hair coloring. A haircut takes on average 30 minutes, while coloring takes 2 hours. The stylist works up to 8 hours in a day, and she needs to make a minimum of $150 a day to pay for her expenses.

    a. Create a system of inequalities that describes the constraints in this situation. Be sure to specify what each variable represents.

    b. Graph the inequalities and show the solution set.

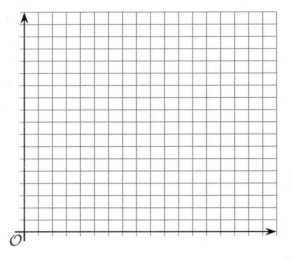

    c. Identify a point that represents a combination of haircuts and and hair-coloring jobs that meets the stylist's requirements.

    d. Identify a point that is a solution to the system of inequalities but is not possible or not likely in the situation. Explain why this solution is impossible or unlikely.

(From Unit 2, Lesson 25.)

Algebra 1

3. Choose the graph that shows the solution to this system: $\begin{cases} y > 3x + 2 \\ -4x + 3y \leq 12 \end{cases}$

A.

B.

C.

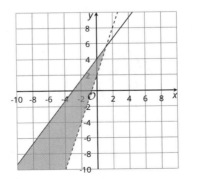

D.

(From Unit 2, Lesson 24.)

4. Match each inequality to the graph of its solution.

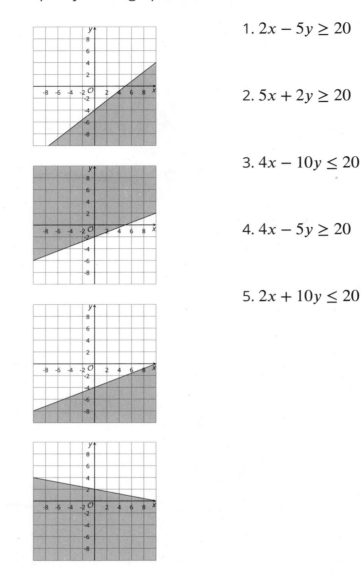

A.

B.

C.

D.

E.

1. $2x - 5y \geq 20$

2. $5x + 2y \geq 20$

3. $4x - 10y \leq 20$

4. $4x - 5y \geq 20$

5. $2x + 10y \leq 20$

(From Unit 2, Lesson 23.)

Learning Targets

Lesson 1: Planning a Pizza Party

- I can explain the meaning of the term "constraints."

- I can tell which quantities in a situation can vary and which ones cannot.

- I can use letters and numbers to write expressions representing the quantities in a situation.

Lesson 2: Writing Equations to Model Relationships (Part 1)

- I can tell which quantities in a situation can vary and which ones cannot.

- I can use letters and numbers to write equations representing the relationships in a situation.

Lesson 3: Writing Equations to Model Relationships (Part 2)

- I can use words and equations to describe the patterns I see in a table of values or in a set of calculations.

- When given a description of a situation, I can use representations like diagrams and tables to help make sense of the situation and write equations for it.

Lesson 4: Equations and Their Solutions

- I can explain what it means for a value or pair of values to be a solution to an equation.

- I can find solutions to equations by reasoning about a situation or by using algebra.

Lesson 5: Equations and Their Graphs

- I can use graphing technology to graph linear equations and identify solutions to the equations.

- I understand how the coordinates of the points on the graph of a linear equation are related to the equation.

- When given the graph of a linear equation, I can explain the meaning of the points on the graph in terms of the situation it represents.

Lesson 6: Equivalent Equations

- I can tell whether two expressions are equivalent and explain why or why not.

- I know and can identify the moves that can be made to transform an equation into an equivalent one.

- I understand what it means for two equations to be equivalent, and how equivalent equations can be used to describe the same situation in different ways.

Lesson 7: Explaining Steps for Rewriting Equations

- I can explain why some algebraic moves create equivalent equations but some do not.

- I know how equivalent equations are related to the steps of solving equations.

- I know what it means for an equation to have no solutions and can recognize such an equation.

Lesson 8: Which Variable to Solve for? (Part 1)

- Given an equation, I can solve for a particular variable (like height, time, or length) when the equation would be more useful in that form.

- I know the meaning of the phrase "to solve for a variable."

Lesson 9: Which Variable to Solve for? (Part 2)

- I can write an equation to describe a situation that involves multiple quantities whose values are not known, and then solve the equation for a particular variable.

- I know how solving for a variable can be used to quickly calculate the values of that variable.

Lesson 10: Connecting Equations to Graphs (Part 1)

- I can describe the connections between an equation of the form $ax + by = c$, the features of its graph, and the rate of change in the situation.

- I can graph a linear equation of the form $ax + by = c$.

- I understand that rewriting the equation for a line in different forms can make it easier to find certain kinds of information about the relationship and about the graph.

Lesson 11: Connecting Equations to Graphs (Part 2)

- I can find the slope and vertical intercept of a line with equation $ax + by = c$.

- I can take an equation of the form $ax + by = c$ and rearrange it into the equivalent form $y = mx + b$.

- I can use a variety of strategies to find the slope and vertical intercept of the graph of a linear equation given in different forms.

Lesson 12: Writing and Graphing Systems of Linear Equations

- I can explain what we mean by "the solution to a system of linear equations" and can explain how the solution is represented graphically.

- I can explain what we mean when we refer to two equations as a system of equations.

- I can use tables and graphs to solve systems of equations.

Lesson 13: Solving Systems by Substitution

- I can solve systems of equations by substituting a variable or an expression.

- I know more than one way to perform substitution and can decide which way or what to substitute based on how the given equations are written.

Lesson 14: Solving Systems by Elimination (Part 1)

- I can solve systems of equations by adding or subtracting them to eliminate a variable.

- I know that adding or subtracting equations in a system creates a new equation, where one of the solutions to this equation is the solution to the system.

Lesson 15: Solving Systems by Elimination (Part 2)

- I can explain why adding or subtracting two equations that share a solution results in a new equation that also shares the same solution.

Lesson 16: Solving Systems by Elimination (Part 3)

- I can solve systems of equations by multiplying each side of one or both equations by a factor, then adding or subtracting the equations to eliminate a variable.

- I understand that multiplying each side of an equation by a factor creates an equivalent equation whose graph and solutions are the same as that of the original equation.

Lesson 17: Systems of Linear Equations and Their Solutions

- I can tell how many solutions a system has by graphing the equations or by analyzing the parts of the equations and considering how they affect the features of the graphs.

- I know the possibilities for the number of solutions a system of equations could have.

Lesson 18: Representing Situations with Inequalities

- I can write inequalities that represent the constraints in a situation.

Lesson 19: Solutions to Inequalities in One Variable

- I can graph the solution to an inequality in one variable.

- I can solve one-variable inequalities and interpret the solutions in terms of the situation.

- I understand that the solution to an inequality is a range of values (such as $x > 7$) that make the inequality true.

Lesson 20: Writing and Solving Inequalities in One Variable

- I can analyze the structure of an inequality in one variable to help determine if the solution is greater or less than the solution to the related equation.

- I can write and solve inequalities to answer questions about a situation.

Lesson 21: Graphing Linear Inequalities in Two Variables (Part 1)

- Given a two-variable inequality and the graph of the related equation, I can determine which side of the line the solutions to the inequality will fall.

- I can describe the graph that represents the solutions to a linear inequality in two variables.

Lesson 22: Graphing Linear Inequalities in Two Variables (Part 2)

- Given a two-variable inequality that represents a situation, I can interpret points in the coordinate plane and decide if they are solutions to the inequality.

- I can find the solutions to a two-variable inequality by using the graph of a related two-variable equation.

- I can write inequalities to describe the constraints in a situation.

Algebra 1 iM KH

Lesson 23: Solving Problems with Inequalities in Two Variables

- I can use graphing technology to find the solution to a two-variable inequality.

- When given inequalities, graphs, and descriptions that represent the constraints in a situation, I can connect the different representations and interpret them in terms of the situation.

Lesson 24: Solutions to Systems of Linear Inequalities in Two Variables

- I can write a system of inequalities to describe a situation, find the solution by graphing, and interpret points in the solution.

- I know what is meant by "the solutions to a system of inequalities" and can describe the graphs that represent the solutions.

- When given descriptions and graphs that represent two different constraints, I can find values that satisfy each constraint individually, and values that satisfy both constraints at once.

Lesson 25: Solving Problems with Systems of Linear Inequalities in Two Variables

- I can explain how to tell if a point on the boundary of the graph of the solutions to a system of inequalities is a solution or not.

Lesson 26: Modeling with Systems of Inequalities in Two Variables

- I can interpret inequalities and graphs in a mathematical model.

- I know how to choose variables, specify the constraints, and write inequalities to create a mathematical model.

Glossary

bell-shaped distribution
A distribution whose dot plot or histogram takes the form of a bell with most of the data clustered near the center and fewer points farther from the center.

bimodal distribution
A distribution with two very common data values seen in a dot plot or histogram as distinct peaks. In the dot plot shown, the two common data values are 2 and 7,

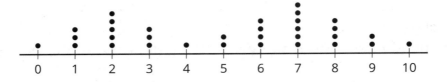

categorical data
Categorical data are data where the values are categories. For example, the breeds of 10 different dogs are categorical data. Another example is the colors of 100 different flowers.

constraint
A limitation on the possible values of variables in a model, often expressed by an equation or inequality or by specifying that the value must be an integer. For example, distance above the ground d, in meters, might be constrained to be non-negative, expressed by $d \geq 0$.

distribution
For a numerical or categorical data set, the distribution tells you how many of each value or each category there are in the data set.

elimination
A method of solving a system of two equations in two variables where you add or subtract a multiple of one equation to another in order to get an equation with only one of the variables (thus eliminating the other variable).

equivalent equations
Equations that have the exact same solutions are equivalent equations.

Algebra 1   **iM KH**

equivalent systems

Two systems are equivalent if they share the exact same solution set.

five-number summary

The five-number summary of a data set consists of the minimum, the three quartiles, and the maximum. It is often indicated by a box plot like the one shown, where the minimum is 2, the three quartiles are 4, 4.5, and 6.5, and the maximum is 9.

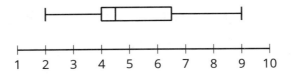

model

A mathematical or statistical representation of a problem from science, technology, engineering, work, or everyday life, used to solve problems and make decisions.

non-statistical question

A non-statistical question is a question which can be answered by a specific measurement or procedure where no variability is anticipated, for example:

- How high is that building?

- If I run at 2 meters per second, how long will it take me to run 100 meters?

numerical data

Numerical data, also called measurement or quantitative data, are data where the values are numbers, measurements, or quantities. For example, the weights of 10 different dogs are numerical data.

outlier

A data value that is unusual in that it differs quite a bit from the other values in the data set. In the box plot shown, the minimum, 0, and the maximum, 44, are both outliers.

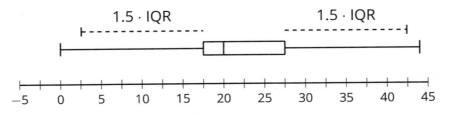

skewed distribution

A distribution where one side of the distribution has more values farther from the bulk of the data than the other side, so that the mean is not equal to the median. In the dot plot shown, the data values on the left, such as 1, 2, and 3, are further from the bulk of the data than the data values on the right.

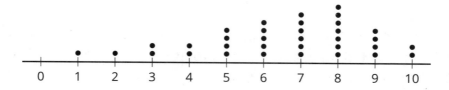

solution to a system of equations

A coordinate pair that makes both equations in the system true.

On the graph shown of the equations in a system, the solution is the point where the graphs intersect.

solutions to a system of inequalities

All pairs of values that make the inequalities in a system true are solutions to the system. The solutions to a system of inequalities can be represented by the points in the region where the graphs of the two inequalities overlap.

standard deviation

A measure of the variability, or spread, of a distribution, calculated by a method similar to the method for calculating the MAD (mean absolute deviation). The exact method is studied in more advanced courses.

statistic

A quantity that is calculated from sample data, such as mean, median, or MAD (mean absolute deviation).

statistical question

A statistical question is a question that can only be answered by using data and where we expect the data to have variability, for example:

- Who is the most popular musical artist at your school?

- When do students in your class typically eat dinner?

- Which classroom in your school has the most books?

Algebra 1 **iM KH**

substitution
Substitution is replacing a variable with an expression it is equal to.

symmetric distribution
A distribution with a vertical line of symmetry in the center of the graphical representation, so that the mean is equal to the median. In the dot plot shown, the distribution is symmetric about the data value 5.

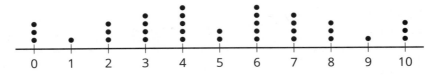

system of equations
Two or more equations that represent the constraints in the same situation form a system of equations.

system of inequalities
Two or more inequalities that represent the constraints in the same situation form a system of inequalities.

uniform distribution
A distribution which has the data values evenly distributed throughout the range of the data.

Attributions

"Notice and Wonder" and "I Notice/I Wonder" are trademarks of the National Council of Teachers of Mathematics, reflecting approaches developed by the Math Forum (http://www.nctm.org/mathforum/), and used here with permission.

Images that are not the original work of Illustrative Mathematics are in the public domain or released under a Creative Commons Attribution (CC-BY) license, and include an appropriate citation. Images that are the original work of Illustrative Mathematics do not include such a citation.

Image Attributions

Pizza, by PublicDomainImages. Public Domain. pixabay. https://pixabay.com/photos/pizza-drink-food-386717/.

Figs and almonds, by pxhere. Public Domain. pxhere. https://pxhere.com/en/photo/79512.

Container Ship, by 127071. Public Domain. pixabay. https://pixabay.com/photos/container-ship-container-ship-537724/.

Asphalt Construction Road Work, by max pixel. Public Domain. max pixel. https://www.maxpixel.net/Asphalt-Construction-Road-Work-3431322.

L.A. County Fair 1262, by Omar Bárcena. CC BY 2.0. wikimedia commons. https://commons.wikimedia.org/wiki/File:L.A._County_Fair_1262.jpg.

Trail mix, by Nennieinszweidrei. Public Domain. pixabay. https://pixabay.com/photos/nuts-food-trail-mix-raisins-cashew-3841539/.

Apple tree, by pxhere. Public Domain. pxhere. https://pxhere.com/en/photo/1168824.

Lawnmower, by pxhere. Public Domain. pxhere. https://pxhere.com/en/photo/281930.

Drought Friendly Garden, by publicdomainpictures. Public Domain. publicdomainpictures. https://www.publicdomainpictures.net/pictures/240000/velka/drought-friendly-garden.jpg.

Quilt, by pixel1. Public Domain. pixabay. https://pixabay.com/illustrations/prize-winning-quilt-triangle-design-958633/.

Citations

Unit 1: One-variable Statistics

Assessment Problem
Channel Seed (2013) http://www.channel.com/agronomics/Documents/
AgronomicContentPDF/GrowthStages%20GuidesChannel.pdf

Lesson 2
Tomato Ripening Times from Ohio State University (2017) https://ohioline.osu.edu/
factsheet/HYG-1624

Lesson 13
A Review of the Welfare of Zoo Elephants in Europe: A Report Commissioned by the
RSPCA (2002)

Lesson 14
Organisation for Economic Co-operation and Development (2018). Health spending.
Retrieved from http://data.oecd.org/healthres/health-spending.htm

Lesson 14
Table 7: offenses known to law enforcement (2016). Retrieved from https://ucr.fbi.gov/
crime-in-the-u.s/2016/crime-in-the-u.s.-2016/tables/table-7/table-7.xls/view

Lesson 15
(For the modeling prompt "Display Your Data") U.S. General Services Administration
(2019). The home of the U.S. Government's Open Data. Retrieved
from https://www.data.gov/.

Lesson 16
Height and Handedness data from Census at School (2018) https://ww2.amstat.org/
censusatschool/index.cfm

Practice Problem 6
American Concrete Pavement Association http://www.acpa.org/

Practice Problem 7
Cross-country Wlkipedia (2018) https://en.wikipedia.org/wiki/
Cross_country_running#Scoring

Practice Problem 9

US Air Force (1995) https://arxiv.org/pdf/1102.4623.pdf

Practice Problem 10

North American Sauna Society (2015) http://www.saunasociety.org

Unit 2: Linear Equations, Inequalities, and Systems

Lesson 26

USDA Food Composition Database https://ndb.nal.usda.gov/ndb/